Katharine Drexel
FRIEND OF THE NEGLECTED

by ELLEN TARRY
illustrated by Donald Bolognese

VISION BOOKS

FARRAR, STRAUS & CUDAHY   NEW YORK

BURNS & OATES   LONDON

Dedicated to
the Cherished Memory of
Sister Mary Inez, S.B.S.

Nihil Obstat:
>   Rt. Rev. Msgr. Peter B. O'Connor
>   *Censor Librorum*

Imprimatur:
>   ✠ Most Reverend Thomas A. Boland, S.T.D.
>   *Archbishop of Newark*

CONTENTS

AUTHOR'S NOTE

Few authors have been priviledged to write a book about the person who has, in the spiritual sense, been the source of their greatest gift—the gift of faith. In writing about Reverend Mother M. Katharine Drexel, this has been my privilege.

It was through the Sisters of the Blessed Sacrament, founded by Mother Katharine, that I discovered the Prisoner of love. I discovered Him Who waits in tabernacles throughout the world for men to come to Him so that He may open the door to His Father through the teachings of Holy Mother the Church.

The awesome responsibility of such a labor of love might have stilled my pen but for the encouragement and help of Reverend Mother Mary Anselm, superior general of the Sisters of the Blessed Sacrament, Mother Mary Pius of St. Mark's Convent, New York City, who first suggested this book, and Sister Mary Timothy of St. Elizabeth's Convent, Cornwells Heights, Pennsylvania, motherhouse of the Sisters of the Blessed Sacrament, who answered my many requests for information.

Had it not been for permission granted to me by Reverend Mother Anselm to use as a source of material *The Francis A. Drexel Family*, edited by the late Sister Mary Dolores, S.B.S., this biography of Mother Katharine could not have been written. If permission had not also been given to me to create dialog, and to enrich certain scenes with details, I would not have felt free to weave a story around the life of one of such sacred memory. All of the major incidents are true. Every character is real.

All of the members of Reverend Mother Anselm's official family at St. Elizabeth's Convent have made a generous contribution in giving me access to documents and publications pertaining to the life of their foundress. I am especially grateful to those sisters at Cornwells Heights and at Torresdale who reminisced and explained as we strolled along paths which once felt the weight of Mother Katharine's feet. They helped me recall much of the story of the early days of this community dedicated to work among colored people and Indians. I had heard that story many years before from the lips of the late Sister Mary Inez, one of the little band of thirteen who accompanied Mother Katharine on the journey from Pittsburgh to open the first novitiate at Torresdale.

A special acknowledgement is made to my friend, George K. Hunton, executive secretary of the New York Catholic Interracial Council, for sharing with me his memories of conversations with Mother Katharine and with her devoted sister, the late Mrs. Edward Morrell, during the years when the Catholic Interracial Council was one of their main interests.

My own spiritual adviser, the Right Reverend Monsignor Cornelius J. Drew, has lent his assistance in many ways to this small effort. I must also thank the close friends and family—my mother and daughter—for bearing with me during the months when I retreated from the demands of everyday life while enjoying the words, actions, prayers, and adventures of Kate Drexel who became Reverend Mother Katharine.

It was many years ago, when June was in the meadows and the sun shone bright in the recreation hall at St. Francis de Sales in Rock Castle, Virginia—just as bright as a July sun is shining on my desk while I write—that Mother Katharine handed me a diploma. Just as that same sun shines today, the same helpful love with which Reverend Mother Anselm and Sister Mary Timothy prepared me for that graduation has flown along the course of years to make this book possible. It is therefore a gesture of appreciation to all of the Sisters of the Blessed Sacrament from one of their own children.

July 24, 1957

Chapter One

An Heiress Grows Up

KATHARINE blinked her eyes, for sleep comes early to a little girl not yet five. It had been some time since Elizabeth had called downstairs to Mama and Papa, and still they had not come up to say night prayers. The Drexels always said their night prayers together, whether they were at home in Philadelphia, or—as they were tonight—in the little cottage at Nicetown.

The covers had been turned down on her bed, and Katharine wished she could crawl between the sheets and pull the soft comforter about her shoulders. But if she did that, she would miss night prayers. And if she let Elizabeth catch her yawning, that eight-year-old big sister would insist that Katharine go to bed.

Outside the cottage the first autumn winds were rustling the leaves. Katharine bent over her doll's crib to pull a blanket over the little figure.

"You'll be sure to catch cold," she sighed. Then one by one she admired the tiny garments in her little favorite's clothes chest.

"A complete wardrobe," Mama had said, "is what a well-dressed doll should have." And that is what she had bought.

When Papa finally came upstairs to say night prayers, he was alone. He made an excuse for Mama but, by that time, both girls were too sleepy to question. A few moments after they had blessed themselves, they were fast asleep.

Papa, Francis A. Drexel, was a very rich man but, as he pulled the covers about his little girls he knew, of course, that all the money in the banks he controlled was nothing compared with them. He knelt beside the bed and said another prayer for God's protection on his children and, "especially tonight," on his wife.

In years to come Katharine and Elizabeth remembered the night Papa had been late for night prayers because of what happened the next morning. It was the second day of October, 1863, and it seemed like the middle of the night when a nurse came to their room.

"The angels were here last night," she began, "and they brought . . ."

"What did they bring?" The girls sat up in bed wide-eyed.

"They brought Mama and Papa and you a little baby—a little baby girl." The nurse laughed as the children jumped out of bed and ran to their mother's room.

The sight of Mama lying in bed, looking so pale and quiet, made them forget about the baby. Katharine and Elizabeth stood at the door until their mother spoke.

"Don't you want to see your little sister?" Mama asked when she opened her eyes and saw the two children.

Katharine put her hand in Elizabeth's and they walked slowly over to the bed and looked at the tiny, wriggling, red-faced baby.

Then Katharine saw the blanket wrapped about the baby and the little dress. "My doll's clothes!" she cried with delight. "*It's* wearing my doll's clothes!"

"Yes, dear." Mama smiled. "The angels brought their gift before we were expecting her. So we had to borrow a few things from your doll. Aunt Elizabeth has already gone to the city to shop for the baby. You don't mind the baby's using your doll's clothes, do you?"

Katharine beamed. She did not mind in the least. It made her feel closer to the new baby who, two days later, on the feast of St. Francis of Assisi, was christened Louise Bouvier Drexel.

From this time on, life in the Francis A. Drexel household revolved around the three little girls— Elizabeth, Katharine, and Louise. Each was precious in her own way to Papa Drexel who, with his brother Anthony, headed the international banking firm founded by their shrewd and talented father, Francis Martin Drexel.

Mama, who had been Emma Bouvier before her marriage, showered affection on the children. One would never have guessed that Katharine and Elizabeth had been born of Francis Drexel's first marriage to Hannah Jane Langstroth, who had died six weeks after Katharine's birth on November 26, 1858.

Katharine was a little over a year old and Elizabeth had just passed her third birthday when their father remarried. With the silent help of Grandmother Langstroth, the young wife did all she could to keep the two little girls from ever knowing that deep, hopeless longing for one gone out of life, or from ever feeling that they were not her own.

Katharine Mary, as she had been baptized, was already answering to the name of Kate when a young Irish girl, Johanna Ryan, came to live with the Drexels and take care of the girls. Joe had been a novice at Eden Hall Convent, but poor health had forced her to leave. She soon became an important member of the Drexel household.

During the winter months the Drexels lived at 1503 Walnut Street, a handsome residence in the fashionable quarter of Philadelphia. Many important men from all over the world came to 1503 to visit Francis Drexel. His wife was a gracious hostess, but her family and her various charities were her first consideration.

Though the word stepmother was never used, Emma Drexel did not attempt to keep Katharine and Elizabeth from knowing that they were not her own children. Each Saturday afternoon Joe took the girls to the home of Grandmother Langstroth, their own mother's mother, who had a special room fitted up with toys for her grandchildren.

On another day each week Mama took all three of the little Drexel girls for a visit with Grandmother Bouvier, her mother, who was said to be "as stately a dame as ever graced the court of Versailles." Grandfather Bouvier had come to Philadelphia from his birthplace of Pont St. Esprit, France, and the French influence was evident in the Bouvier and Drexel households.

There were many Bouvier aunts, but it was the younger ones who spent the most time with the girls while Mama talked with Grandmother Bouvier. There was also Aunt Elizabeth, who had shopped for Baby Louise when she was born, and Aunt Louise, who was Madame Bouvier, a Religious of the Sacred Heart at Eden Hall Convent. And then there was Uncle Michel. He was the youngest of the Bouviers, and Mama had a special reason for loving him so much.

One Sunday afternoon Joe was dressing the girls

for their weekly visit to Grandmother Drexel when she noticed a frown on Kate's brow.

"And why would Kate be frowning?" she asked as she tied the sash on the little girl's dress.

"Maybe she has a stomach-ache," Elizabeth suggested.

"No, I was just thinking," Kate admitted, "that I like the visits to Grandmother Drexel's best of all. I like to visit Grandmother Langstroth and Grandmother Bouvier, too, but . . . but . . ."

"So many grandmothers you don't know which one to choose," Joe smiled. "But, of course, you love them all. Now maybe it's the cookies and nuts and juicy apples Mrs. Drexel always keeps near that big rocking chair of hers that's making little Kate love her so."

"Or maybe it's Tony and Joseph and all the rest of our Drexel cousins who visit on Sunday afternoon," added Elizabeth, laughing.

There was only three years' difference between Elizabeth and Kate, while Louise was five years younger than Kate, but the bond seemed closer between the younger girls, and they spent many hours in rollicking fun.

"How these two little sisters do love each other," Mama Drexel often told Johanna Ryan as she watched Kate tumbling, making funny faces, and doing other tricks which she thought would amuse Louise. The reward was usually a generous shower of laughs which Louise often climaxed with, "Oh, Kate! You are the funniest girl in the world!"

The three sisters always looked forward to hearing the wonderful stories Mama told or read to them. They loved to hear about the time the Bouvier country home had burned to the ground and Mama had helped the old nurse rescue Uncle Michel who had been left in his cradle. No wonder, the girls always thought at the end of the story, Mama loves Uncle Michel so.

Family stories were not the only ones Mama told the delighted girls. She told them about the saints and, though the children were surrounded by luxury, the three of them developed a special devotion to St. Francis, the "Poor Little Man" of Assisi.

It was usually Kate who begged hardest to hear the stories about Francis' love of the poor, of animals, of flowers and plants. Each time the little girl heard about how young Francis sold his father's goods to raise enough money to repair the Church of San Damiano, she put herself in his place. She wondered what Papa Drexel would have said if she had sold one of the treasured paintings done by his own father, or the beloved pipe organ with the beautiful rosewood console, in order to get money for the poor people who were always coming to her mother for help.

The time came all too soon when storytelling had to give way to the more serious business of school. Kate was secretly envious that first day Mama took Elizabeth to the school on Walnut Street conducted by the Ladies of the Sacred Heart. She brooded and lagged about the house. Even when Louise begged for "just one little trick," her solemn older sister paid no attention.

That afternoon Kate was awakening from a long nap when her mother came to her room. "Would you like to go with me to call for Elizabeth at school?" Mama asked.

Kate was thrilled. Joe helped her get dressed quickly and, in a few moments, Mama Drexel and her second daughter were on their way. This was the beginning of a happy custom, and each afternoon Joe stayed with Louise while Kate and her mother called for Elizabeth.

In due time Kate followed in Elizabeth's steps, and there were two little Drexel girls at the Walnut Street School.

From the time Elizabeth made her first Holy

Communion, Kate, too, wanted to receive and began talking about "the happiest day of my life." At that time it was the custom for boys and girls to make their first Holy Communion around the age of twelve. Kate expressed such longing to receive that Mama and the Ladies agreed to allow her this privilege on June 3, 1870, while she was still eleven.

The Ladies of the Sacred Heart made great preparation for the day. Kate and all of the other little communicants were to be confirmed immediately after the Mass at which they had received Holy Communion for the first time. Mrs. Drexel was to play fairy godmother and treat the little girls and their mothers to a communion breakfast at which Archbishop Wood of Philadelphia was to be the guest of honor.

"I wonder if heaven is like this," Kate whispered to Elizabeth when they saw the way the sisters had decorated the school chapel. At the altar rail each communicant's place was marked by candles and flowers. "I'm so happy that I think I'll float right up to heaven."

Kate found, though, that instead of thinking of floating up to heaven, she had to concentrate on kneeling very straight so as to avoid being burned by the flames from the candles or knocking the beautiful bouquet to the floor. She managed, though, and received the Sacrament with cautious, but trembling, joy.

It wasn't long before Kate and her sisters came to understand that Francis Drexel was a very important man to many people. Board meetings were often held at the Drexel home, and financiers like J. P. Morgan of Wall Street fame and E. T. Stotesbury of the Philadelphia banking clan were among the many who visited frequently.

These duties never kept Francis Drexel from joining the girls and their mother in night prayers when he was home. And once each month he led them up the church aisle to the communion rail. At that time it was unheard of for lay people to receive Holy Communion more than once a month.

During the winter, when the family lived at 1503, Papa Drexel went directly to his room each afternoon when he returned from the bank. He would close the door, stay there for some time, and then go to the music room. Beautiful notes would pour from the organ with the gold-looking pipes that Francis Drexel loved so.

While Papa was in his room, neither Mama nor

the girls dared to open the door. One day, when Kate was tiptoeing past, a maid saw her.

"He's not asleep," the woman whispered.

"Isn't he?" Kate asked. She had always thought that her father napped when he came home from the bank.

"No." The maid shook her head. "But I'm the only one who knows what he does in there. If you promise not to tell a soul, I'll tell you. Follow me to the pantry downstairs."

Kate was a bit worried because the servant had spied on her father. She wasn't sure it was right. And she wasn't sure, either, that she could promise not to tell her mother. But the maid didn't wait for Kate's promise.

"I'd forgot whether I'd finished my dusting," the woman whispered, "and I rushed to his room thinking I'd get it done before he came home from the bank. But wouldn't you know that would be the day Mr. Drexel had come home early? I opened the door and there he was—the Mister himself—on his knees praying. He was praying so hard, mind you, that he never even heard the sound I made. I was so surprised to see him, you know. And I've been back since, always accidental like—not to peep—and every day he's doing the same thing, praying."

Kate's first summers were spent at Nicetown, where the baby Louise had been born. It was considered the country then, but now it is part of the city of Philadelphia. There, in Fishers Lane, was a comfortable house which Papa Drexel rented from Mrs. Susan Ole. The Drexels went to Fishers Lane in the late spring and lived there through the summer until the trees were aglow with the red-golden hues of autumn.

Mrs. Ole lived in a cottage at the rear of the main house. She kept a large vegetable garden, chickens, a cow, pigs, and a dog or two. It was in Fishers Lane that Kate and her sisters came to know and love animals.

Shooing the chickens and racing the dogs was fun, but Jenny and Dap, two donkeys who pulled the girls' little cart, were the most popular. Each morning Jenny and Dap announced the dawn of a new day with their gentle braying. At breakfast time two shaggy heads were thrust inside the open dining room window, and the donkey serenade continued until Papa or the girls offered bits of bread from the table.

The house in Fishers Lane was lighted by kerosene lamps, and to Kate and Elizabeth fell the task of fetching the oil from the store. Jenny and Dap always carried them in the cart. As payment, the girls were allowed to treat themselves to old-fashioned ginger cookies. The most exciting part of the trip to the store took place after Jenny and Dap had trotted past an old mill, the last object that could be seen from the porch of the Fishers Lane house. Then Elizabeth would give the signal and the two girls would straddle the donkeys.

On the return trip, the adventure was sometimes interrupted when the cart would hit a rut in the road and kerosene would slosh through the spout of the can onto the cookies. Then the only thing to do was stop at the next pump, wash the cookies off, and eat them all before the oil had time to soak in.

Kate was never sure what she should do when mischievous boys trotted along beside the donkeys and then jumped into the empty seat while the girls rode astride. She knew, though, that Elizabeth would make sure her whip was in plain view when she called, "Get out, please. Get out at once!" And the boys always did get out *at once*. Elizabeth knew how to speak with authority.

Every day after lunch the girls took a nap. Once afternoon prayers had been said, Mama would read to them until their eyes closed and they drifted off to sleep. Sometimes Kate dreamed about Saint Francis and far-away Assisi. Sometimes it was her other storybook-hero, George Washington. More than once she went to sleep whispering, "Let perpetual light shine upon George Washington. May his soul rest in peace." It was a practice she was to continue for the rest of her life.

Kate loved to get dressed up late in the afternoon and wait for Papa on the side porch of Mrs. Ole's house. Then the family would go for a drive in the carriage until time for supper.

But there were also things about life at Fishers Lane which Kate found not so pleasant. She dreaded sewing lessons, and there were many hours when she might have been riding Jenny or Dap, or listening to the pigs squeal, which had, instead, to be spent practicing her piano lessons.

Looking backward many years later, Kate decided that 1870, her twelfth year, was one of the most eventful of her early life. The nation was still in the midst of troubled times growing out of the War Between the States which Kate had been too young to remember. But to Katharine Drexel 1870 recalled not the memory of the bitter Reconstruction Era but thoughts of her first Communion and of the coming of Mary Ann Cassidy, who was to tutor the Drexel girls at home.

"Miss Cassidy lives in Camden with her widowed mother and sister," Mama Drexel had explained to Papa. "A lovely young woman—well educated and really exceptional."

"But don't you think she will find it difficult to come across the river from Camden each day and spend practically all her time teaching three little girls? That's a rather confining job for a young woman."

"Now, Francis, it's all settled. Miss Cassidy is very eager to come, and my sister, Louise, and I are convinced that she is exactly the right person to mold the characters of our three darlings."

"I can see," Francis Drexel laughed, "that Mary Ann Cassidy has been away from County Kerry long enough to make two staunch friends—you and Madame Bouvier."

And so began Mary Ann Cassidy's happy association with the Drexel family. In winter, when the family was at 1503, Miss Cassidy came from Camden each morning to spend the day with the Drexel children.

It was also in 1870 that Francis Drexel bought a ninety-acre farm on the Red Lion Road at Torresdale, Pennsylvania, which was to be called St. Michel.

Before the girls saw it, Mr. Drexel enlarged and remodeled the three-story house. A roofed porch was built across the entire front of the house. At one end of the porch was a huge Dutch door, the glass of the upper part protected on the outside by elaborately wrought iron grillwork.

Above the front door Mr. Drexel installed a statue of St. Michael, his spear and shield carved in Caen stone. A mosaic floor was laid just inside the entrance. To the right was a drawing room and then huge folding doors, which opened to reveal a large and beautifully appointed dining room.

At the head of the first flight of stairs was a recessed window. Because the house had been placed under the special guardianship of St. Michael, patron saint of Uncle Michel Bouvier, Francis Drexel commissioned a Philadelphia firm to install in this window stained glass representing the archangel.

The Drexels always used the French pronunciation of St. Michel (*San Mee shel'*) in speaking of the Torresdale home. Joe was the only one who refused to use this pronunciation. "No Ryan would

call St. Michael anything but 'Michael'!" she insisted.

The sprawling grounds around the house were
converted into well-kept lawns with shade trees.
Cottages were built for the servants, and a spacious
stable, carriage house, and barn were put up.

Francis Drexel and his wife spared neither time
nor money in furnishing and decorating the interior
of the house. Mama saved a special day for the three
little girls and Joe to have their first glimpse of the
country place.

After she made her speech about the name, Joe
had nothing but praise for St. Michel. "And sure
it's just like a palace," she insisted. "Fit for any king
or queen—or princesses," she added when she saw
the expression on the faces of the girls.

It was soon after the Drexels occupied St. Michel
that Mama suggested a plan which made Kate very
happy.

Chapter Two

The Mountains Cast a Shadow

ELIZABETH and Kate were to share a bedroom at St. Michel, just as at 1503 Walnut Street. "Don't you think, Mrs. Drexel," Miss Cassidy suggested soon after their arrival, "that Elizabeth should have a room of her own? After all, she's fourteen now."

"That will come later," Mrs. Drexel replied. "Kate is too young to be alone yet, and if I put Louise in the room with her, they will do tricks and giggle half the night. I'd really like Kate to spend more time with Elizabeth. There are times when she amazes me with the seriousness of her thinking—especially in spiritual matters. Her devotion to St. Francis of Assisi has given her a burning desire to help the poor."

"Her devotion to St. Francis, yes, *and* the beautiful example set by her own mother and father," Miss Cassidy declared with feeling.

"God has been good to us," Emma Drexel replied simply. "We must share that over which He has made us guardians and never forget our responsibility to others, especially to our employees." Then she told Miss Cassidy what she had in mind for the two older girls. It was not until later that she told Elizabeth and Kate.

St. Michel had settled down to the stillness which comes at the end of a day well spent. Prayers had been said, and Joe was in Louise's room putting her to bed when Mrs. Drexel slipped into the older girls' room.

"You look so mysterious, Mama," Elizabeth said after they had chatted for a while. "I hope Miss Cassidy isn't going to scold about our spelling."

Mrs. Drexel put an arm around each of her girls. "Few mothers have been blessed with such wonder

ul daughters. That is why I decided on the plan I
m going to tell you about."

Kate's thoughts raced along as she tried to im-
gine what her mother was going to tell them. Per-
aps, she thought, we are old enough now to help
ive out clothes and groceries to the people who
ome to the back door of 1503 for help. We've
een wanting to do that for so long. But we're at St.
Michel now, and Mama wouldn't tell us about that
ntil we're in the city again. Surely she's not going
o tell us that it's time we were going away to school.

"You need not worry about your spelling for the
moment, Elizabeth. And you can erase that frown,
Kate," Mama went on, smiling. "Seriously, I have
een concerned about the children of the men and
women who work for us. There are no sisters nearby
o instruct them, and I feel a grave responsibility
ecause we brought several of the families out from
he city. I was hoping that you girls would help me
o start a Sunday school."

Elizabeth threw her arms about her mother's
eck. "Nobody ever had such a wonderful
mother!" she declared. "You think of everybody's
welfare. We'd love to teach Sunday school,
wouldn't we, Kate?"

"Oh, yes!" Kate breathed. She was so happy she

could hardly speak. "Yes!" Had not her beloved St
Francis gone out and preached and taught the
people? Now she would really be following in his
footsteps.

For the next few days Kate and Elizabeth were
busy with plans. A special part of the laundry was
set aside for classes. It was agreed that Kate would
teach the younger girls and Elizabeth would instruct
the older ones.

"Don't you think boys have souls, too?" their
father teased.

"The decision to start with the girls was mine,"
Emma Drexel admitted. "Of course the boys have
souls. But they are also full of stubbornness. The
boys, young or old," and the wife gave her husband
a knowing glance, "might not want to come to
Sunday school because they are told to do so, but
with the girls there, the boys will be sure to come
around—even if it's just to see what's happening.'

In less than a month almost fifty boys and girls
were crowding into the laundry on Sunday after-
noons. After the lesson, Kate led them up to the
parlor where Elizabeth took her place at the piano
and they sang their favorite hymns. Kate had never
enjoyed practicing the piano, or taking vocal lessons

but after they started the Sunday school she was glad that her mother had insisted.

Mary Ann Cassidy was very proud of her two oldest pupils. She had made a rule some time before that during the summer, when there were no classes, the girls should write her twice a week. That summer the letters were full of news of the Sunday school, and Miss Cassidy kept up with the activities of her pupils, at the same time checking on their penmanship, composition, sentence structure, and spelling.

In the early fall of 1870, a letter from Kate told Miss Cassidy that everybody at St. Michel was excited. Archbishop Wood was to pay a visit to the Drexel country home!

It was not until the day of the archbishop's visit that Mrs. Drexel told the girls that the visitor was to celebrate Holy Mass at St. Michel the following morning. The carriage was ordered, and Joe and Kate rode over to Eden Hall. Madame Bouvier's superior there had consented to supply the altar linens and sacred vessels.

"It's sure a great honor," Joe kept telling Kate, "to have the archbishop himself sleeping under the same roof with you. But to have the Holy Mass said right in your own parlor—that's *really* something! Only a few people would ever get that permission. But then, the Drexels are very special. People all over Philadelphia talk about the good work they do."

The news spread quickly, and the next morning the folding doors of the dining room had to be opened. The parlor was too small for the family and all the workmen who came to assist at this special Holy Sacrifice.

The next big event at St. Michel was the closing session of Sunday school. Miss Cassidy had suggested in one of her letters that the pupils be given badges, or prizes, for attendance and application. Mrs. Drexel offered to buy prizes, and the last Sunday at St. Michel was selected as the appropriate time.

It was while her middle daughter was making the list for gifts to be given out to the Sunday school pupils that Mrs. Drexel decided Kate had inherited some of her father's shrewdness and practical way of thinking.

It had been apparent for years that Elizabeth was growing to look more and more like the Langstroths, who were Dutch. Her complexion, hair and eyes were lighter than those of the other girls.

From the time Louise was toddling, her striking resemblance to her mother was noticeable. As she grew older, her golden curls might have been richer in hue and her thin lips a whit less severe than her mother's. Still, she was a small replica of Emma Drexel.

Kate was "Papa's girl." Like her father, she had a determined chin, with deep-set and thoughtful blue eyes. She had her father's finely chiseled nose, but where his was straight, there was the slightest tilt at the extreme end of Kate's.

"Only about half of them came every Sunday," Kate told her mother as she made out the Sunday school gift list, "so only the faithful need be rewarded."

"Don't be a meany," Elizabeth spoke up. "We can give them all something. Mama said we could."

"It would be wrong to encourage those who came only when they felt like it," Kate insisted seriously. "Mama said we could serve cookies and lemonade after the prizes are given out. Then nobody will be left out. But we can't encourage the lazy ones, can we, Mama?"

Emma Drexel agreed with Kate, though she tried to conceal her surprise. She was also surprised when Kate selected practical prizes like pencil boxes, gloves, and prayer books.

I suppose she has passed the giggling age, her mother thought. And I'm sure her father will be proud of the way she is spending his money.

All of the Drexels were sad when moving day came and it was time to leave St. Michel and return to the city. Most of the city servants went ahead to Philadelphia to prepare for the family's return. Papa was at the bank, so Mama and the girls and Joe were left to follow in the carriage with what pets they were allowed to carry to 1503, plus the most valuable table silver and assorted bundles. The trip was a lark and took away some of the sting of leaving St. Michel.

Soon after returning to 1503 Walnut Street each fall, Papa Drexel took his family for a short trip to some section of the United States that he thought would prove interesting to the girls.

"It's easier to learn history and geography by traveling," he reminded Miss Cassidy, who was afraid the trips might interfere with the girls' studies.

While California, Maine, Colorado, the Great Lakes region, New Orleans, and the White Mountains were merely names on the map to most boys and girls, to Kate and her sisters they were places they had visited and could talk about. It was the White Mountains which seemed to offer Kate the most satisfying adventures. In one of her biweekly letters to Miss Cassidy while the family was in the White Mountains, she wrote that it was Sunday morning and that they were setting out for a climb to Thompson's Falls where they would say special Sunday prayers. Kate and Louise ran ahead of Elizabeth and their parents.

"Anybody can find the way to Thompson's Falls," Louise grumbled as she stopped to tear off a briar that had stuck to her heavy sock. "I wish we could go to Tuckerman's Ravine. The guidebook says it's spooky there."

"I wish we could, too," Kate sighed. "But the guidebook says that the path is blind and difficult and that children should be left at home. I heard Mama when she read that part to Papa."

"I've been to Thompson's Falls before," Louise pouted as she broke into a trot, "and I don't want to go there today."

Suddenly they reached a fork in the road. "One of these paths leads to Tuckerman's Ravine," Kate said, almost to herself. "And the other leads to the falls. But I can't remember which one. We'd better wait till the others catch up with us."

"Oh, come on," Louise urged. "It won't be long before they'll be calling to us to wait anyhow." And the two girls took the road that led up and up the side of the mountain.

Soon they heard a familiar call and turned to see Elizabeth running to catch up with them.

"Papa is furious," she said breathlessly. "A man just came along who knows this country, and he said we're on the road to Tuckerman's Ravine. He's going there, too, and has offered to guide us. Mama wants to go, but Papa says he couldn't take you two on such a dangerous climb."

"Oh, wouldn't it be fun to go to the ravine?" Louise cried. "I can climb as well as Papa. Let's go ask Mama to tell him to let us go."

"The guidebook did say the road was marked by flares," Kate remembered. "Maybe that will influence him. We'll tell Mama."

They headed back to their parents. The man who had volunteered to guide the little party was reassuring Mr. Drexel, and this gave Kate and Louise time to talk privately with their mother.

"Oh, Mama," Kate begged, "can't we go to the ravine? Can't you get Papa to let us go?"

"This man," Mama whispered, "seems to be doing the job. He just told your father he's sure the path is marked by flares. Perhaps we will get to see the ravine after all."

The conference was interrupted by the booming voice of the guide. "We'll take the first turn to the left, ladies. Then up we'll go!"

And up they went along moss-covered pathways, across creeks and streams that seemed to appear suddenly and then end just as suddenly. Kate was puzzled when she first saw her father pull a piece of paper from his pocket, tear it into bits, and fasten the bits onto the trees.

Surely Papa is not afraid, Kate thought. We can see the flares up ahead, and I've never known him to be afraid of anything. Never!

As they crawled over a pile of broken hemlocks obstructing the path, Louise, too, noticed her father as he fastened bits of paper onto the trees.

"Look at Papa," she whispered to Kate. "What's he doing with the paper?"

"He's marking the trail."

"What for? You don't think he's afraid, do you?"

"Papa is never afraid," Kate declared. As they jumped across another smaller pile of fallen hemlocks, she told her sister about a day at the seashore when she had been standing on the beach afraid to go into the water. Papa had swung her over his shoulders and waded out into the surf.

"I had my arms tightly around Papa's neck," she continued. "The salt spray splashed into my face and I choked a little. Papa ducked, and as I went under the water, he met a great big wave. It dashed against us, then covered us both. I thought I was drowning, so I closed my eyes and held on to Papa's neck as tightly as I could. I could feel his arms around me, and when he told me to open my eyes, we were safe on the beach again. I told him how strong his arms were, and he said our heavenly Father's Arms were around both of us, and that was what saved us."

"Maybe he just doesn't think the Lord's Arms will reach way up here and keep us from getting lost," Louise giggled.

"Shame on you!" Kate scolded her little sister. "How dare you say such a thing!"

"Oh, Kate, you know I was only teasing. You used to be so much fun. You're just too—too sancti . . . What is that big word Joe said you were getting to be?"

"So you and Joe have been talking about me?" Kate laughed.

"I know!" Louise cried. "Joe said you were getting sanctimonious and that I shouldn't worry because I'm not. Joe says she doesn't think I ever will be. And I don't want to be—if it means no more fun!"

Kate wondered why Joe had said she was sanctimonious. Only her mother knew about her love for St. Francis and that she always asked God to look with favor on the soul of George Washington because he had been our first president. Still Mama always turned to her when she wanted Louise coached on special prayers or proper behavior at Mass. Kate wondered if Joe had said Elizabeth was sanctimonious, too.

The girls walked along in silence for another mile, pushing back the thick bushes in their path. A few feet behind came the rest of the party. The girls hadn't even noticed that flares no longer marked the path until they heard their father's voice rise above that of the volunteer guide.

"I'm *not* going another step!" Francis Drexel declared. "I didn't want to come, but you assured me you knew the path. I will *not* jeopardize the safety of my family."

"I told you he wasn't afraid," Kate whispered to Louise. "He's thinking only of us."

Elizabeth called to her sisters. "Mama is sure we can sight the flares," she said, "if only we go a little farther. Kate, you come with me, and Mama will take Louise. We'll stay within calling distance. The poor man doesn't know what a stone wall Papa can be. They'll be arguing for some time. Meanwhile, if we find the path, there'll be no objection to going on." Elizabeth made sure that each of her sisters had a stout stick to push back the underbrush.

Emma Drexel and the girls disappeared among the thickets while her husband and the guide argued back and forth. Francis Drexel watched the man as he drew a map on the ground with a twig he had broken from one of the trees.

"I don't care how many times you've made the trip," Mr. Drexel finally told the guide. "We are off the path now, and I will not be responsible for leading my wife and daughters in such a hazardous climb."

"We've sighted the flares again!" Mama emerged from one direction, with Louise following, as Kate and Elizabeth beat back another clump of bushes.

"We spotted them, too! Three flares!" Kate cried exultantly. "Come, Papa, we'll be sure to find the path now."

"You have also lost the bottom of your skirt."

Her father pointed to a torn flounce. "And there's a scratch on your face. I will *not* go another step!"

Emma Drexel pleaded with her husband to come with them to the point where he could see the flares, but even her endearing terms failed to move him. Kate knew there was no need to plead any more. Her father had made up his mind, and now he was getting annoyed with them for being so persistent.

"Let's say our prayers over by those rocks," Kate suggested. She pointed to a small chain of boulders on the mountainside, and Elizabeth and Louise followed her.

The sight of the kneeling children fingering their beads as their young voices rose in the most beautiful of prayers, softened Francis Drexel's scowling face and dulled his wife's disappointment. The guide went on his way while the parents joined the children. Together they chanted praises and thanksgiving to the heavenly Father Whose strong Arms were always around them.

The descent was made easier by the pieces of paper Papa had fastened onto the trees. The sun was setting when they glimpsed the hotel. Without a spoken agreement the group stopped and looked up at the peaks before them—Mounts Madison, Jefferson, Adams, Clay, and Washington.

Kate moved closer to her mother. "They're so—so big and bold," she whispered. "Even the sunset can't make them soft. They're like the time that was and the time that will be."

"Yes," her mother answered softly, "like the solidarity of eternity."

"That's what Miss Cassidy said one day when we were talking about mountains—that they make you think of eternity. Before," Kate admitted, "it was always hard for me to think what eternity meant. It just means the time that was and the time that will be—forever and ever. Isn't that right, Mama?"

That night when the girls were asleep Emma Drexel was sharing Kate's comment on the mountains with her husband.

"This visit has been worth a year of geography lessons," he said. "I think it's about time we took them to Europe. That will be our next big trip."

"Kate will love that. Especially the shrines," Emma added thoughtfully.

"Won't the other girls enjoy Europe?" Francis Drexel asked. "Why did you say Kate would enjoy the shrines? She's—she's only a child. What did you mean?"

"I'm not really sure." The wife smiled as she realized her husband was reluctant to admit that his daughters were growing up. "We've had a long day. Perhaps this is something we can discuss another time."

"I—Emma—I hope you don't think me unduly stubborn for not going on to Tuckerman's Ravine," he said. "Your life and the lives of the children are in my keeping. I cannot take unnecessary risks. I hope you were not too disappointed."

His wife smiled. "Perhaps you were right after all. It would have been dark when we returned. And that moment at sunset, when we all stood looking at the mountains before us, would have been lost." Emma Drexel sighed deeply. "That moment is a precious memory. If for no other reason, it was worth missing the trip to the ravine to have Kate come to understand the meaning of eternity."

Chapter Three

The Drexels in Europe

KATE was sixteen when the final plans were made for the trip to Europe. It was during the winter of 1874 that she heard her father discussing the trip with her mother. Later she spoke to Elizabeth.

"We couldn't possibly go to Europe until after we leave St. Michel," Kate insisted. "Who would teach Sunday school?"

"Don't worry. Mama knows we wouldn't want

to give our jobs to anyone else," Elizabeth said. "I'm sure we won't leave until fall. Joe told me the other day that she's going with us. That means Miss Cassidy will stay here to be in charge of everything, and we won't have to bother about lessons while we're in Europe. Isn't that wonderful?"

"The only difference," Kate reminded her sister, "is that we'll be writing our lessons in the form of letters twice a week."

Kate was right. A few days later their mother showed them a note from Miss Cassidy about the letters she expected to receive from Europe.

Elizabeth moaned. "At least it won't be long before *my* school days are behind me. But poor Lou and Kate! And you know, Mama, Kate will describe every cathedral and every shrine in Europe, and Miss Cassidy will consider it a matter of conscience to give her good marks, no matter how dull the letters are."

Kate said nothing, but she was sure that Miss Cassidy would not find her descriptions of churches and shrines dull. It was just as well, she thought, that she hadn't told Elizabeth how badly she wanted to visit the Vatican and the little town of Assisi.

"I should remind you, girls," Mrs. Drexel went on, "since we're speaking of lessons, that I have asked Mademoiselle de St. Marsault to double up on your French. Once you are in Europe you will appreciate Mademoiselle as much as you appreciated your music after you started the Sunday school at St. Michel."

One rainy afternoon at St. Michel, when Papa was late returning from the city, Mama amused the girls by telling about their honeymoon in Europe. The bride and groom had gone to Pont St. Esprit to visit the Bouvier relatives.

"Imagine the expression on your father's face when the first male relatives threw both arms about him and kissed him, first on one cheek and then on the other," Emma Drexel recalled, laughing. "But he soon realized it was the local custom and learned to offer dutifully each cheek every time a new kinsman was presented."

"Kate, you pretend you are Papa," Louise began, "and I'll be the Bouvier relative. Elizabeth, you be the grandmother who ushers the relatives in."

In a few minutes the girls were going through the motions of turning the incident into a comedy. Elizabeth opened the door to Louise, who greeted Kate with mock seriousness as she said, *"Bonjour, Monsieur Drexel,"* threw both arms around her scowling sister, and kissed her on both cheeks.

"The only thing which rings true in that performance," Mama laughed, "is the way Kate looks. Your father looked much the same way when the first Bouvier greeted him. But Mademoiselle de St. Marsault will tell you that *'Bonjour, Monsieur'* would not be affectionate enough."

"It would be, *'Bonjour, mon cher François,'* " Kate decided, forgetting to erase the frown.

"You still look just like Papa," Elizabeth declared, laughing, and the others agreed.

Emma Drexel told the girls of the visit to the Austrian town where Papa's father, Francis Martin Drexel, had been born. On the wall inside his old home was a beautiful picture of the Blessed Virgin and Child which Grandfather Drexel had painted when he was a lad of eighteen. Mama told them about Ireland, and Paris, and about the day in June when she and Papa had been presented to the Holy Father, Pius IX, in private audience. The kindly pope had blessed their marriage.

"My dear Mama," Louise, who loved to use big words, began, "our appetite for Europe is *enormous!* When do we sail?"

"After we have all done an *enormous* amount of packing," her mother replied. "And now we had better dress for dinner. Your father will surely arrive soon."

Mr. Drexel booked passage on the *Scotia* of the Cunard Line for the latter part of September, 1874.

Joe, who was as excited as the girls over the trip, was furious when she heard that Liverpool was the first port they would touch and that London was the first city they would visit.

"Who wants to go to *that* place?" she grumbled. "Ireland is the place for anyone to go who really wants to *see* something!" Joe continued to grumble until Mrs. Drexel explained that only one day was to be spent in London since Mr. Drexel wanted the family to enjoy Switzerland before the coldest weather set in.

The girls left the shores of their native America in high spirits. They were all seasoned land travelers, but they suffered a bit of seasickness the first few days. Once that difficulty was behind, they were free to enjoy the serenity of the ocean.

A visit to Westminster Abbey filled most of the day the Drexels spent in London. Mrs. Drexel told Joe that she might remain at the hotel and rest, or feel free to go to the abbey with the family.

Joe insisted on going and confined her grumbling to the ears of the three girls. But she could not

control her anger when the family group stopped
in front of the tomb of Queen Elizabeth.

"Now, what would sensible people like the
Drexels be doing," she muttered, "standing here
looking at auld Betsy's monument?" And the loyal
daughter of Erin made a number of guesses as to the
present whereabouts of "auld Betsy."

Later, as they stood in front of the tomb of one
of the monks who had lived before the time of
Henry VIII, Joe's anger broke out again. The sexton who was showing them through the abbey,
weary from the task of deciphering inscribed names,
referred to the deceased as a "jawbreaker." Mrs.
Drexel saw the danger signal in Joe's eyes. "You girls
walk ahead with Joe," she suggested. "We'll catch
up with you in a little while."

The girls propelled the indignant Joe out of the
hearing of the sexton. "I wish the walls of the whole
dingy place would fall on his head," she spluttered
and fumed. "Why couldn't he call the good priest
respectfully by his own name the way any good
man would?"

"I'm glad to get out." Kate tried to change the
subject. "All of these tombs make me think of a
monument store."

"It serves you right." Joe wouldn't be sidetracked. "I still can't figure why anybody in his right mind would want to come to this place—not that I mean to be disrespectful of the Mister and Missus," she added.

The parents found the girls laughing when they rejoined them. Johanna had given the London visit a comical twist.

Mrs. Drexel and her girls were delighted when they reached Lausanne, Switzerland, to find an old friend from Baltimore, Miss Carrere, waiting for them at the hotel. Miss Carrere had been living in Italy for some years. Because of her knowledge of the continent, Mr. Drexel had invited her to join the party.

"Caro," as the girls called her, knew of their father's love of the organ, and she led them to great cathedrals and musty little churches full of medieval statues where they heard wonderful organ music. It was one of the greatest joys of the trip for Francis Drexel.

The girls looked forward to seeing the famous clock when they visited Bern, and Louise was up before the rest of the family that first morning in the historic home town of renowned Swiss watchmakers.

"Hurry!" she kept saying. "The procession of

bears starts on the hour. There might be a crowd in front of the tower and then we couldn't see them come out."

There were minutes to spare when the Drexels reached the clock tower. Only a few other people were waiting for the traditional procession. Then, at the stroke of twelve, the first of the miniature animals emerged from the clock.

To Louise it was great fun, but Kate thought the performance a bit childish and was secretly relieved when Elizabeth announced, "It's very nice amusement for *children!*"

"Perhaps American *children* are not amused so easily," her mother said as she smiled.

In gay Vienna, Papa Drexel escorted his two oldest daughters to the theater where they saw a presentation of *Oberon*. But, as Kate later confided to her teacher in what the girls called her "weekly agonizings," Vienna would always be remembered humorously because of one small excursion.

It didn't seem at all humorous, though, the morning that Kate and Elizabeth decided they would dare to set out alone and unchaperoned to find an English-speaking confessor.

"There's that little church not too far from the hotel," Kate remembered. "We can go to Mass and hen inquire about a confessor. I do wish we could peak German though. How will we make them understand what we want?"

"We'll decide after we get there." Elizabeth was n a hurry to get started.

Mass was either over or had not begun when the girls arrived at the almost-empty church. They waited a while after they had said their prayers, then walked around the building until they found a door which seemed to lead to the sacristy. A few gentle knocks brought no response. They knocked harder. Still no response. They hammered violently until a boy appeared, astonished at seeing two refined-looking young ladies who seemed bent upon knocking in the sacristy door.

Elizabeth walked over to the confessional, pointed to it, and repeated in German a sentence their father had taught them: "Is there an English-speaking priest?"

"He almost laughed," Kate whispered to Elizabeth when the boy had disappeared. "And you used the German pronunciation that Papa said was correct."

After a long wait the young sacristan reappeared and addressed the girls in rapid German which neither understood. They did catch the names of St.

Anne and St. Catherine. Perhaps that meant there
was an English-speaking priest at either of those
churches.

"He might have brought one of the priests out,"
Elizabeth complained as they walked back to the
hotel. "Now we'll have to look through the guide
books to find out where those churches are."

Johanna Ryan loved nothing more than sur-
mounting obstacles, and while the girls were looking
through the one guidebook, she found the Church
of St. Catherine listed in another. When they
started out again, Joe was their confederate.

A cross-looking sexton was locking the door
when the trio arrived at St. Catherine's. Once more
Elizabeth asked for an English-speaking priest as
her father had taught her. The old sexton shrugged
his shoulders and slammed the door.

Again they consulted the guidebook, then set out
to find St. Anne's. Someone mistook them for
Italians and directed them to an Italian hospital at
the opposite end of the city. Their next attempt
landed the hapless three in a convent where they
interrupted the nuns in the midst of community
prayers. None of these good religious spoke or
understood either English or the Drexel-Ryan
brand of German.

After a number of attempts Kate and her companions found the Monastery of St. Anne. A kindly brother admitted them, listened to their request, and evidently took them for sight-seers. He conducted them through labyrinthian corridors until they reached an immense iron door which squeaked with the rust of age when it was opened—the better for the three amazed girls to view the vault of Marie Antoinette!

The little party returned to the hotel, but they were not yet ready to give up the search.

That brother was wearing the brown robe of St. Francis, Kate kept thinking. Somehow I feel that Francis' brother will lead us to what we want.

She confided in Joe and Elizabeth, who agreed that it was too late to start out again but that they would try the next morning.

Emma Drexel knew there was nothing unusual about her girls' plans to go to Mass, but she could tell by the satisfied expression on Joe's face that this morning some new adventure was afoot. Knowing Joe to be a formidable chaperon, however, Mrs. Drexel had not a single fear for their safety.

Once more the determined three made their way to the Monastery of St. Anne. Once more Kate rang the bell, and once more the brother who had

treated them to a view of Marie Antoinette's vaul
opened the door.

He gave a deep sigh and clasped his hands, looking heavenward as if for help to understand the request which Elizabeth repeated once again. He
motioned to them to wait, and Kate felt confident
that St. Francis was interceding.

In a few moments the brother returned, led them
down a dimly lighted hall which seemed to have no
end, and turned into another just as long and just as
dim.

"And whose tomb do you think he's taking us to
this time?" Johanna's voice seemed to echo through
the silent corridor.

"Where's that undying faith you're always
bragging about?" Elizabeth asked.

"Well," Joe grinned, "I'm holding on to my
beads."

Kate put her finger to her lips and frowned at Joe
and Elizabeth. She thought she saw in the distance
a shadow and the glow of a candle. The shadow
walked toward them, and they were face to face
with a tall, elegant-looking priest whose handsome
features and long grey beard caught the warm glow
of the candle which he held in his hand. His pierc-
ing black eyes studied the three faces before him.

"Americans?" he asked slowly.

"Yes, Father," Elizabeth began, only to be interrupted by Joe.

"They're the Drexels from Philadelphia," Joe rattled away. "The Holy Father himself gave Archbishop Wood permission to say Mass at their house on Walnut Street and at the place in the country. Not only that, but the archbishop sleeps under the same roof with them when he comes out to the country to say the Holy Mass."

Kate was embarrassed, but she saw that the priest did not understand what Joe was saying. This time she was the one who stated their mission. In broken English the priest haltingly explained that he did not understand their language well enough to hear confessions. Kate was beginning to think St. Francis had failed her when the priest asked if they could confess in French.

Once the confessions were over, the brother emerged from the darkness and led them through the long halls for the last time.

"No American priest's 'Go and sin no more' ever sounded more beautiful," Kate said.

"My French was no better than his English," Joe admitted. "I hope St. Peter doesn't hold this confession against me on Judgment Day."

Kate longed to visit Assisi, but every time she mentioned it, something intervened before her parents promised to make the trip. Her father was anxious to reach Italy, but he spoke only of Florence and Rome. Kate, remembering that Louise had said she was sanctimonious, decided to wait and say nothing more.

Soon after entering Italy, the Drexels stopped overnight in Bologna. The next day they went for a tour of the city and, as they approached the Church of St. Catherine, a guide told them that the relics of St. Catherine were reposing there.

"Do you mean St. Catherine of Siena?" Kate asked. "She is my patron saint."

"Yes, yes!" the man answered. "St. Catherine is there—seated on a chair. Would you like to pray before her? I will see if arrangements can be made to open the small chapel."

Kate was thrilled at the prospect of viewing the body of her patron saint and took out her beads to offer up a Rosary of thanksgiving. She had barely finished a decade when the guide returned with a priest who smiled and bowed as he led them to a little chapel where he opened the door with a huge key which hung at his waist.

Only four candles illuminated the chapel, and on

he altar sat the figure of St. Catherine. The Drexels
stared in wonderment.

The priest bowed again before he genuflected and
disappeared.

"The body was placed here ten years after her
death," the guide whispered. "It was never em-
balmed and is just as limber as it was 450 years ago."

"Look." He pointed to a red spot on the lips of
the figure whose face and hands, even though they
had turned black, remained firm and unwrinkled.
"That is the spot where our Lord kissed her."

It was only after Kate and her family had returned to the hotel, looked through their guide-
books, and talked with the chambermaid, that they
discovered the saint they had seen was not Catherine
of Siena but Catherine of Bologna.

"I've never heard of St. Catherine of Bologna,"
Kate told her mother.

"Then perhaps it was a lesson well worth learning," Mama replied, knowing full well the sting of
Kate's disappointment.

Later Kate thought again of the visit to St.
Catherine's chapel. Perhaps I set too much store by
earthly reminders of the saints, she concluded. After
all, the important thing is that the saints are glorified
in heaven and that we can pray to them no matter

where we are. Maybe that's why Papa hasn't said anything else about the visit to Assisi.

On December 8, 1874, the Drexel family observed the feast of the Immaculate Conception in Florence. That afternoon they drove out through olive fields with ripe purple fruit shining among the green foliage to the Chartreuse Monastery.

Kate thought she had never seen so picturesque a sight as the high wall that encircled the grounds. It was covered with roses, and now and then they passed an opening in the wall through which they could see the purple Apennines.

As they approached the old monastery standing on a hill overlooking the countryside, Kate decided it reminded her of a proud general standing at attention as his army passed in review.

"To see these venerable old monks pacing the cloisters with their white cowls drawn over their heads," Kate wrote Miss Cassidy, "or to hear them chanting office in the old walnut choir, just as they did 500 years ago, seemed more like something to be read and wondered about, than to be actually witnessed."

Mr. and Mrs. Drexel listened as the girls talked about the old monastery. Louise wished she could paint a picture of the monks saying the Divine Office. Elizabeth was impressed by the evidences of good housekeeping in an all-male establishment. But Kate surprised them all. She soberly announced, "If I were a man, I would enter the order on the spot. But I would want access to a good library and a suite of rooms with a view of the Apennines."

"That," Emma Drexel declared, "is probably why you would not enter the order—even if you were a man. I have yet to hear of an order which induces would-be novices with good books and idyllic views."

The Drexels spent Christmas of 1874 in Naples. Accustomed to snow and cold at Christmas, they found it difficult to get into the spirit of the season. As warm sunshine stole into the hotel windows, and as they watched the glistening blue waves of the bay, it seemed more like a holiday at the beach than a Christmas away from home.

"It will only make you appreciate next Christmas at St. Michel more," Mrs. Drexel told her homesick girls.

The girls were to remember always the colorful celebrations which took place in Naples on Christmas Eve. Against a blue Italian sky studded with

stars, hundreds of sky rockets ascended heaven-
wards, while showers of tiny red, blue, and green
lights were thrown from the balconies into the
streets below. From their hotel suite they could hear
voices singing in the distance. The music reminded
Kate of the gay young days of St. Francis' life
when he expressed himself in serenades.

The young year of 1875 found Kate and her
family in Rome for the long-expected visit to the
Vatican. Mr. Drexel made the acquaintance of a
helpful French priest who arranged for them to
have an audience with the Holy Father. Johanna
was as excited as the girls over the prospect of
actually seeing the pope. Again and again she asked
Mrs. Drexel about her visit to the Vatican during
her honeymoon.

The priest who acted as their guide suggested
that they bring a new silk calotte which Louise, as
the youngest member of the family, could present
to the Holy Father. He also suggested that the
family address the pontiff in French.

On the morning of the audience Mr. Drexel bor-
rowed from the hotel a silver tray on which the
white silk skullcap was placed. Then the family
proceeded to the Vatican where their priest-guide

showed them through the various anterooms and halls leading to the small room where the audience was to be held.

Kate's parents were pleased at the dignified manner in which the girls and Joe behaved, in spite of their excitement at the spectacle of ornately dressed Swiss guards bearing the pope through the halls on their shoulders before setting him down in their midst.

When Pope Pius IX came to the Drexel group, Louise stepped forward, offered the calotte, and said in her best French, "Very Holy Father, will you accept this calotte and give me yours?"

Pope Pius IX laughingly replied in English, "But why do you want my cap? See, the one you brought me is too thin, too small. What would you do with mine—put it in your pocket?"

"Oh, no," Louise replied without prompting, "I want to take it home with me—to America!"

As the little girl spoke, the delighted pontiff playfully tossed his cap onto Louise's head and made as if to pass on. It was then that Joe, in a fit of enthusiasm, fell to the floor, pressed forward, and threw her arms around the Holy Father's knees as she cried, "Holy Father—praise God and His blessed Mother—my eyes have seen our dear Lord Himself!"

Joe had acted impulsively out of unquestioning faith and intense devotion. She was so sincere and deeply moved that neither Mr. nor Mrs. Drexel mentioned the incident until some time later, and they forbade the girls to do so either.

En route to Paris the family stopped at Pont St. Esprit, the birthplace of Grandfather Bouvier, and assisted at Mass in the same little church where Emma Drexel's father had worshipped.

When they reached Paris, Kate was delighted to see the ease with which the French included religion in their everyday lives. They never seemed in too much of a hurry to stop for a visit to the Blessed Sacrament.

The family teased Kate because she insisted that when she went shopping she never could find what she wanted. Despite the many beautiful clothes and objets d'art in Parisian shopwindows, Kate claimed that the dress, coat, hat, or picture she wanted always seemed to have been sold or was missing. Again and again her sisters called Kate the flag waver, for she always compared sights, customs, and even shops to those in her native land.

It was only after Papa announced that he thought it was time for Elizabeth to make her debut that the girls went on the shopping spree that their mother had anticipated. Even then, Kate and Louise, who had some years to wait before being introduced to the social world, showed a preference for country clothes over the high fashion of Paris. In the end it was a letter from Miss Cassidy which helped Mrs. Drexel arouse in her younger girls an interest in feminine frills.

"Miss Cassidy writes that the city is agog with plans for the celebration of the 100th anniversary of the Declaration of Independence," Mrs. Drexel announced one morning at breakfast. "The exposition will be held next year."

"And we have decided," her husband added, "to wait until January of the centenary year, Elizabeth, to present you to society. With visitors in the city for the centennial, the occasion should be more festive. Though it is not a thought I relish," and Mr. Drexel's eyes twinkled, "it is highly possible that more than one or two eligible young men will present themselves at 1503 Walnut Street. I suppose I will have to start looking with new eyes at my friends who have sons."

Elizabeth blushed at her father's speech, but Kate seemed little impressed. Louise was the only one of the three who spoke out. "Boys," she decided, "are not half as much fun as you, Papa. And as long as we have you and Uncle Michel and Uncle Tony, and our cousins, it doesn't matter whether the boys come to 1503 or not."

Emma Drexel smiled. She knew how much Louise's childish declaration of loyalty and devotion had pleased her husband. She knew, too, though, that Louise was going through a stage which would soon pass. Elizabeth was already showing signs of becoming a young lady. But she was not sure about Kate.

The double lure of Elizabeth's debut and the centennial aroused the girls' interest in clothes and, in spite of the snow and cold weather which slowed the carriages on the street of Paris during the winter of 1875, Kate and her sisters bought everything their mother thought a "well-outfitted young lady should have."

In the midst of the shopping, Kate thought from time to time of St. Francis. They had not visited Assisi after all. She thought of how he had cast aside his fine clothes and rejoiced in poverty, and sometimes these thoughts made her uneasy. She was glad when her parents decided to forego visits to Scotland and Ireland and return to her beloved America.

Chapter Four

The Gay Centennial

By the time June was in the air, Kate and her family were back at St. Michel. Recollections of the trip were a daily topic, and Kate made a packet of the pictures of famous castles, churches, and museums they had visited. After classes began in the fall, she showed them to Miss Cassidy, along with the leaves and flowers she had plucked from various palace gardens and monuments.

Some weeks later, Miss Cassidy handed Kate a large package. In it were all the letters, edited and corrected, which her pupil had written from Europe. Kate copied them and put the collection in a scrapbook, illustrated with the pictures and pressed leaves and flowers. Mrs. Drexel told Miss Cassidy later how pleased she was that Kate had made the scrapbook.

"Once Kate begins a project," Miss Cassidy replied, smiling, "she seldom, if ever, stops until it's completed. In fact, she applies herself so well"—and Miss Cassidy laughed—"that sometimes she's almost *tiresomely* applicative."

"When she's gay, she's very gay," Mrs. Drexel said, "but when she's serious, she's very serious. She seems to go from one extreme to the other. I only hope we can help her to find her vocation in life without too much delay. Kate is nearly seventeen now, and a mother always wants to see her children established before . . ." Emma Drexel broke off and sighed. ". . . before she leaves them."

After the Drexels' return to Philadelphia, preparations were begun for Elizabeth's introduction to society. Louise poked fun at what she called Elizabeth's "new grown-up ways," but Kate felt a vague, inexpressible sadness at the absence of her older sister from the classroom.

As the Christmas before the centennial approached, there was much talk about the previous sunny Christmas in Naples. The house at 1503 had been redecorated, and greetings and laughter of friends and relatives echoed through the beautiful rooms.

Kate and Elizabeth were pleased to help their mother prepare gifts for the needy. The Drexels always referred to their mother's pet charity of regularly helping scores of people who presented themselves at the back door of 1503 Walnut Street as the "Dorcas," in memory of Dorcas in the Acts of the Apostles who had "devoted herself to good works and charity."

Mrs. Drexel kept a woman regularly employed to care for the needy who sought her aid. Johanna, too, insisted on being a part of the Dorcas and prided herself on being able to tell the difference between the deserving and the "spongers."

As the girls stuffed stockings for the children who were to have candies, fruit, and perhaps a toy or two, Kate reminded Elizabeth of one of the reasons they had always been happy to see Christmas come. "Looking at this candy," she said, "reminds me that

Christmas was the only time Mama ever allowed us to have it."

"That's because too much candy isn't good for the teeth," Elizabeth decided. "It always seemed so strange that we could have cookies—but no candy except at Christmastime."

"Well, we've seen the necessity for the music lessons," Kate admitted, "and for the French. So we will probably see some day the wisdom of eating candy only once a year."

"Speaking of French reminds me," Elizabeth replied, "of what Mama told me this morning. I am to be presented on the feast of Le Petit Noel."

"On the Epiphany! Oh, how wonderful!" Kate dropped the stocking she was stuffing and embraced her sister. "I still wish we could have been twins. Let's see. First there will be Christmas, then New Year's Eve to usher in the centennial year, then New Year's, and six days later the Epiphany and your party. Oh, Elizabeth, isn't it great to be living now and to have such a wonderful mother and father?"

"Don't forget I have two first-rate sisters as well," Elizabeth laughed, and when Emma Drexel came into the "Dorcas storage room," she found the girls chattering away.

By New Year's Eve the spirit of the coming

celebrations had cast a happy spell over everyone at 1503 Walnut Street. The girls and the servants rushed about like bees in a busy hive. At lamp-lighting time Kate and Elizabeth ran from room to room with glowing tapers to be sure that each gas jet was lending its yellow glow to the celebration in observance of 100 years of American freedom.

In front of the first-floor dining room door, Louise, bedecked in five small flags which she had purchased out of her allowance, danced in jubila-tion. Kate and Elizabeth unwrapped the enormous flag their father had purchased for the celebration, and Hance, the butler, helped them take it upstairs. The Stars and Stripes were then draped gracefully around the balustrade of the balcony overlooking Walnut Street.

"The house must look beautiful," Elizabeth said as they ran down the stairs once more.

"And so—so patriotic!" Kate added with a vehe-mence that made Elizabeth laugh and caused Louise to cut short the capers with which she was amusing the elderly butler.

"Katie is a flag waver!" she sang out. "Katie is a flag waver! Flag-waving Katie!"

"At least I wave my flag at the appropriate time," Kate retorted, "but here you are dancing all over the house decked out in flags." And all three of the girls burst into laughter.

The last meal of 1875 was served early that evening, and the girls asked their mother if they could go outside and walk by the house to see how it looked aglow with lights and draped with flags.

"Perhaps Papa might take us for a walk later," Mama promised, "and then we could see how both Chestnut and Walnut Streets look. It should be a sight for all Americans to cherish, not only my three." Emma Drexel smiled fondly at her girls.

The last day of the year had been a busy one for Francis Drexel, but the plea in the eyes of his three girls made it impossible for him to refuse his wife's request.

Some of the houses in the area were lighted and decorated, but before the Drexels had gone far, they could see that more than a few of their neighbors were either lazy or negligent.

"How could they?" Kate wailed. "At least three-fourths of the houses on Walnut Street are dark. And the mayor ordered that every citizen of Philadelphia should illuminate and drape his house on the evening of the 31st of December! Oh, what would George Washington think?"

"If you don't lower your voice," Louise joked,

"you'll probably wake George Washington up."

Even Francis Drexel found it difficult to suppress his amusement when Kate replied, "Wouldn't that be thrilling? Then I wouldn't have to pray for the repose of his soul any more. I would have all of those prayers to give to somebody else."

Emma Drexel was glad when they came to Chestnut Street and George Washington was discarded as a topic of conversation. Kate was pleased that nearly all of the Chestnut Street houses and buildings were brilliantly lighted and properly draped with the Stars and Stripes, which were waving in all directions. The store windows, too, were decorated with red, white, and blue, and the street was crowded with people. From the top of the Chestnut Street Theater a huge calcium light shed its glow on the people below and upon the flags of all nations draped across the building. The walls of many of the houses were agleam with Chinese lanterns.

The girls wanted to walk all the way to the historic old State House, but their father adopted his "enough-is-enough" air, and Mama suggested that it was past Louise's bedtime.

"I'm always the one who has to go to bed," Louise sighed as the family retraced its steps. "The night I make *my* debut I intend to sit up until morning. That will be more fun than having a party—just being allowed to sit up until *I* decide it is time for me to go to bed."

Francis Drexel gave Louise a reproving look, and his wife turned the conversation into a safer channel until they got home.

Kate and her sisters were awakened that night by the boom of cannons, ringing church bells, and hundreds of penny trumpets announcing the death of the old year and the birth of 1876. The girls sat up in bed and listened until the last bell had been rung and most of the penny trumpets were silent.

"If only," Kate wished, "we had seven-league boots, we could go down to Independence Hall and watch the hoisting of the United States flag."

"*You* can go to Independence Hall," Elizabeth mumbled as her head hit the pillow. "*I* am going to sleep."

On the morning of January 6, the house was already astir when the girls arose. An extra corps of servants had been hired for the banquet at which Francis Drexel was to present his eldest daughter to society.

Louise loved excitement, and Miss Cassidy, who was slightly inclined to favor her youngest pupil, had trouble getting her to the classroom. Kate had to force herself to keep from laughing at the ridiculous answers Louise gave during class. More than once Miss Cassidy consulted the watch pinned to her shirtwaist, and nobody was sad when she announced that classes were dismissed.

"Oh, Elizabeth must be too excited for words," Louise cried as she rushed out of the classroom. "I'm going to see how she looks."

On the first floor men were busy draping the chandeliers with green smilax vines and pinks. The dining room door was partly open, and Kate was surprised to see the soon-to-be-debutante methodically counting the best silver forks and spoons.

"Aren't you excited at all?" Louise asked. "I know my cheeks would be as red as roses if I were going to be presented tonight."

"When the time comes," Elizabeth announced with a slight air of importance, "you will feel differently."

Kate smiled as Louise mimicked her older sister, and Miss Cassidy decided this was a good time to hustle the younger girls off for a late afternoon ride.

When the girls returned, the house was in readiness. The sight of swallow-tailed waiters flying around in search of tumblers and plates amused them no end. Miss Cassidy permitted them to look at the dining room table which was elegantly set with large India dishes and a handsome gilt candelabra at each end. There were side tables filled with fancy cakes, meringues, jellied chicken, chicken salad, and more dainty concoctions than the girls could recognize.

Waiters were darting in and out of the room, heedless of the girls and Miss Cassidy. So heedless did the waiters seem that Louise decided to sample one of the cakes. But when she reached for it, she felt a frozen stare on her. One waiter was not so busy that he could fail to notice a perky thirteen-year-old bent on snatching a cake, even if she *was* the daughter of Francis A. Drexel. Louise gave up after a second futile attempt.

At 7:30, Kate and Louise peeped over the banisters for a look at their parents who stood in the library awaiting the first guest. Johanna, who had already quarreled with one of the swallow-tailed waiters, joined the girls but refrained from comment. She was enjoying one of her silent moods.

"They look so funny," Louise decided. "Papa looks gloomy. Mama's dress is pretty—but she doesn't look happy, either. What's wrong with them, Joe?"

For a few seconds Kate thought Joe was going to continue to sulk, but Louise had a way with the temperamental Miss Ryan.

"Well," Joe began, "it's like this. When a young bird learns to fly, and his wings get strong, he soon flies away from the nest. Your mother and father know it, and it's eating at their hearts. For sure it's martyrs they look like. *That's* what's wrong with the two of them!"

"But what have birds and martyrs got to do with Mama and Papa?" Louise wanted to know.

Joe and Kate smiled at each other in the way of two adults dealing with a child too young to understand. They were saved from explaining by the appearance of Miss Cassidy. She suggested in her most gentle voice that there was still time for the girls to run down and say good night to their parents.

Elizabeth, beautiful in her simple white gown with a single strand of pearls at the neck, joined her parents while Kate and Louise were in the library. It was only then that Kate saw her mother and father smile. Joe was right, she thought. They *were* sad because their "birds" were learning to fly.

After the party, the Drexels settled down to the pace of living imposed upon a family with a daughter who has recently been presented to society. There was a rush of invitations, callers, intimate dinner parties.

The date for moving to St. Michel was postponed because the tenth of May had been set aside as Centennial Day. This was the event the family had looked forward to for so long. The day was to begin with a parade and end with formal Centennial Day ceremonies.

Like most of their neighbors on the square, the Drexels gathered on the upstairs balcony to watch the parade. Walnut Street had been aroused from the lethargy which had irked Kate so much on New Year's Eve, and now a slight breeze waved the flags which hung from every residence.

Louise kept listening for the roll of drums and started waving the small flags she held in each hand as soon as she heard the music. At the head of the procession were the mayor and the members of the City Council, all handsome, broad-shouldered men looking aristocratic as they rode past on prancing horses.

The companies of infantrymen that followed made a colorful picture, some dressed in grey, some in red and blue, and others in blue and white. They were followed by sunburned Marines in blue suits and white hats, and then by a regiment of men wearing yellow knee breeches, black cutaway jackets, and three-cornered George Washington hats.

Louise clapped, and the two older girls thrilled over the picturesque war horses drawing bulky field artillery and the drum and bugle corps. Romantic-looking aides-de-camp galloped the entire length of the parade with messages from one general to another.

There must have been a practical joker among the officials in charge, for, at the very end of the parade celebrating America's independence from Great Britain, rode a figure representing John Bull. Fat and sneering, he passed by as the last band played the national anthem.

The Drexels were startled when Johanna, standing just inside the balcony with Miss Cassidy, shouted, "*This* for you," as she waved her fist menacingly and stepped forward so as to be in full view. The crowd shouted and applauded, and Kate thought she saw the sneer on John Bull's face shift briefly to a half smile.

When the parade was over, there were many callers at 1503 Walnut Street. Dinner was followed by a mad rush to get Kate dressed before nine o'clock. She was to join the party her father's sister, Mrs. Lankenau, and her husband had made up to attend the centennial ceremonies.

Kate reached the Lankenau residence in time to be presented by Uncle John to the German ambassador. She never quite understood the pronunciation Uncle John gave the ambassador's name, but she knew he was a baron, and she was impressed by the manner in which he snatched off the three-cornered hat he was wearing and bowed with stiff formality.

A spring shower had fallen shortly before dusk, and the grounds around the centennial buildings were wet enough to make walking uncomfortable. The ladies in the party held their dresses as high as they dared in order to avoid the mud underfoot.

A friend of Uncle John's had offered the party the use of his apartment in the main building, and Uncle John was fussing and fuming because his friend was not at the appointed place when the group arrived. Kate, who walked alongside the uniformed baron, had resigned herself to standing in the mud to see the centennial opening. Uncle John's friend soon appeared, however, and led the party to his quarters.

"And there," Kate later told Miss Cassidy, "were twenty other people to whom he had extended the same invitation—all talking and looking out from the long line of windows into the large square between Memorial Hall and the main building. It was not long, though, before we were comfortably seated.

"To our left," she continued, "we could see a platform extending from the main building. Almost a thousand men and women were waiting there to sing the centennial chorus. In the meantime, an orchestra played the national air of every country represented by an ambassador. You should have seen the baron when they played *Heil dir im Seigeskranz!*

"As far as the eye could see, there were people pushing and jostling each other. Every inch of ground was covered. Between the main building and Memorial Hall was a sort of alley, which was set aside as a passageway for the invited guests. A line of soldiers had to press continually against the crowd to keep the people back.

"But the funniest of all," Kate laughed, "was the sight of about twenty people who escaped the mad crush by climbing up onto the two large prancing bronze horses in front of Memorial Hall. There was a slight drizzle, and there they were with open umbrellas sitting on the backs, necks and raised legs of the noble animals.

"We heard a loud clapping of hands and even

louder hurrahs. Uncle John's friend announced that the emperor and empress of Brazil were approaching. I got a good look at the empress. She was a little above average in height, middle-aged, with a kind, benevolent face. She was dressed in lilac silk and wore something which looked like a white wreath on her head.

"I was still looking at her when thunderous applause broke out, and there was President Grant and the whole diplomatic corps. It—it was so American!" Kate declared. "The band played *The Star-Spangled Banner* while everybody stood at attention.

"Then there was utter silence. Bishop Sidney repeated the prayer which had been composed especially for the centennial. I just kept thinking that, in spite of the rain, God must have been smiling on the whole ceremony. One hundred years of independence!"

Kate was so carried away with her recollections of the Centennial Day ceremonies she had not noticed that Louise and Elizabeth had entered the room.

"What about George Washington? Don't you think he was smiling, too?" Louise teased and ran down the hallway before Kate could catch her.

Chapter Five

The First Cloud

THE centennial year passed and the Drexels were happy to settle down to a more tranquil manner of living. Relatives and near-relatives had found it convenient to visit anyone within radius of Philadelphia's Fairmount Park during that memorable year, and the Drexel hospitality had attracted scores of visitors, including many priests.

One morning as the girls were finishing breakfast there was a great commotion at the back of the house. Several workmen were carrying a huge crate upstairs. The girls were curious to know what was in it, but Elizabeth, who no longer attended Miss Cassidy's classes, had to go to discuss menus with the cook. Kate had to rush to the classroom to study for final examinations. Louise was the only one who had time to investigate, but it did her no good, for the crate remained tightly nailed.

That afternoon Emma Drexel had the servants open the crate which had been placed in the room Kate shared with Elizabeth. The girls were over-joyed when they recognized a beautiful stained glass window that an English firm had exhibited at the centennial. The central figure was a young girl weaving. An older woman leaned forward as if giving instructions. Their dresses were in Biblical style, and the Drexels decided that the artist had been inspired by the visit of the Virgin Mary to St. Elizabeth. The window was named "St. Elizabeth" and installed in the girls' bedroom.

Wise Mrs. Drexel intended that her daughters be impressed by this lovely model of feminine industry, and she soon called the girls together for a confer-ence.

When Mama began to discuss a division of household duties, the girls thought she was joking or lead-ing up to some pleasant change in routine.

"What is there for us to do?" Louise asked, after she realized her mother was serious. "There are so many servants here and at St. Michel."

"And what will the servants think when we come snooping around?" Elizabeth asked.

"Kate, have you no questions or objections?" the mother asked patiently.

"I remember," Kate replied, smiling, "the music lessons we didn't want to practice and the many times when we objected to spending extra hours in the classroom with Mademoiselle de St. Marsault. But when we were in Europe, especially the day in Vienna when I was looking for an English con-fessor, we understood why you had insisted that we have lessons in French. So . . ."

"So, dear Mama," Elizabeth, who seemed to grow closer to her mother each year, interrupted, "we know you must have some good reason in mind. We will all be Mother's little helpers because she is the best mother in the world and always knows what's best for her darling daughters."

Kate knew that her mother was pleased as she went on to make assignments for each girl. Louise, who loved long walks with her dogs trotting along beside her, was given the responsibility of the farm and garden when they were at St. Michel. During their stay in the city, she was to be concerned with the outside appearance of the house and of the yard.

"You spend most of your waking moments out doors anyway," her mother reminded. "And you, Elizabeth, would rather ride and eat than anything else. So you will supervise the kitchen as well as the stables."

Kate, who was more inclined than her sisters to enjoy pulling loose threads together, was appointed housekeeper. Hers was the task of attending to all of the details connected with the interior of the house. She was to oversee the butler, maids, seamstress, laundress, coachman, and any servant brought in for special occasions. The girls had to make weekly reports and, though she accepted recommendations, their mother reserved the right to make final decisions when emergencies arose. The girls enjoyed being helpful, and Emma Drexel was delighted with the way they discharged their duties. She was happy, too, in the knowledge that she was preparing them for the day when they would be presiding over their own homes.

Kate passed Miss Cassidy's final examinations

and school days ended for her on July 2, 1878. She was formally introduced to society in January, 1879, when she was twenty. Her debut followed much the same pattern as the earlier party given for Elizabeth. It was comforting to Kate to have Elizabeth with her at the coming-out party, and most of the invitations which came to 1503 thereafter were addressed to the "Misses Drexel." Kate admitted that she was secretly glad when the first season was over and they left the city for St. Michel where the months always seemed to pass much too quickly.

"Each year," she laughingly told her sisters, "just when I think the boys and girls in the Sunday school class are ready to sprout wings, it's time to close. Never," she insisted, "are they the same when we come back to St. Michel for Christmas."

Kate loved the old farmhouse and always felt a pang when moving day arrived.

"As much as I hate leaving St. Michel," she remarked the day the family was returning to the city for her second social season, "this is the only time we're all together when we drive over the pike and pass so many familiar sights."

"But the horses seem so slow today," her mother commented, "and we hardly have time for extended

sight-seeing. I hope we won't keep your father waiting for dinner."

"Mama," Elizabeth began as she leaned over to
brush her mother's cheek with a kiss, "you always
say the same thing. Yet Papa is always playing the
organ when we get home, and we have plenty of
time to wash and dress before the music stops and
he realizes we're in the house."

Emma Drexel had to laugh with her girls. Miss
Cassidy and Joe, who were waiting at 1503, commented on their flushed cheeks when they arrived.

"It's proud I am to see a little color in your
mother's cheeks," Joe confided to the girls while
they were dressing. "I haven't liked the looks of her
for a long time. She's much too pale and thin to suit
me."

"It couldn't be the strain of worrying over one
Johanna Ryan, could it?" Elizabeth laughed away
the idea of her mother's not looking well.

"Joe's forever making gloomy observations."
Louise was annoyed. "Mama always looks beautiful!"

"I want you to know one thing." Kate spoke
seriously, though the other girls had spoken with
humor. "If anything ever happened to Mama, I
would enter the convent."

"I guess you're satisfied," Elizabeth told Joe. "You've just driven my sister into the cloister!"

"Praise be!" Joe cried. "The organ has stopped and your father will be going down to dinner any minute. Hurry, or we will all catch it."

Johanna decided not to mention Kate's comment to Mrs. Drexel because she could not very well explain how the conversation had come up. She did, however, speak of it to Bishop James O'Connor. Kate corresponded regularly with His Excellency, who had been pastor of the church the Drexels attended when at St. Michel. He later became the first bishop of Omaha, Nebraska. Joe told him what Kate had said the next time he came to St. Michel to say Mass.

The bishop knew that Francis and Emma Drexel had instilled in each of the girls a deep sense of responsibility for their fellow man. He also believed that, of the three, Kate felt this responsibility most keenly. He prayed that God would grant him the wisdom to counsel Kate wisely when the proper time came.

Emma Drexel was pleased that so many of their friends invited Kate and Elizabeth for visits. The two girls were often the center of attraction at house

parties in Long Branch, Asbury Park, and othe
fashionable gathering places. Their father usuall
joined the girls to accompany them home, an
Uncle Michel, whom they secretly called Th
Prince, often served as their escort.

There was a constant exchange of letters betwee
the girls and their mother, and she was delighted tha
they met so many young women of their own age
She was concerned, though, that they seldom men
tioned young men in a serious way. When she spok
of it to her husband, he replied quickly, and with
touch of annoyance, "There is plenty of time fo
that, Emma."

Kate and Elizabeth were visiting relatives at th
seashore during the summer of 1880 when Emm
Drexel had a dream about her second daughte
which seemed so real that she awakened callin
Kate's name.

"What's wrong, my dear?" Francis Drexe
gently awakened his wife. "You know the girls ar
at Long Branch."

"Oh, it was the dream, Francis." Emma Drexe
looked around to be sure she was awake. "It was so-
so beautiful—but yet so strange."

"The way you were calling Kate I wasn't sur
what was happening." Papa Drexel chuckled. "

guess you're beginning to miss your young lady daughters. Well, they'll be home soon." Mrs. Drexel could tell from the tone of his voice that he was closing the subject.

"But don't you want to hear about the dream?" he asked.

"The dream? Why, no one pays any attention to dreams, my dear." Kate's father smiled affectionately at his wife. He seemed a little amused.

"But this dream was different, Francis. I saw the painting of a door, and it was so beautiful! It was the kind of door we often saw in Europe in the walls of church sanctuaries—the kind which led to a reliquary. The one I dreamed about was bedecked with many rare and dazzling jewels, but it was locked. I was curious to open it and learn what relics were kept there. That's where Kate came in."

Emma Drexel was so serious that her husband began to listen intently. "Kate and Elizabeth were with me," she continued. "I asked Kate for the key, and her face was almost as radiant as the jewels when she said, 'Jesus holds the key, for this is the door of His heart. He opens only to those who knock and ask.'

"It was so real—just as if she were right here in the room, Francis."

"Then why were you calling her name so desperately?" he asked.

"Because of what happened after Kate spoke. Elizabeth laughed at her pious interpretation and said it was nonsense. Poor Kate looked so hurt I thought she would cry. But when I tried to console her, the picture started fading and I remember calling out to Kate."

"I must say, Mrs. Drexel, that you are a remarkable dreamer!" Kate's father commented.

"I only wish I understood its meaning," Emma Drexel said. "Sometimes I think our Lord is trying to tell me something."

"About what?"

"About Kate."

Francis Drexel put an arm around his wife. "Now, Emma, the trouble is that Kate is a middle child and we don't know what to do about her. As much as I hate to admit it, we both know that Elizabeth will probably marry one of those boys who always seem to be calling lately—the Smith boy, or one of the others. Louise will do whatever she decides—whether it be to head Drexel & Sons, or marry. But we're not sure about Kate, and that's what's worrying you. We shall just have to wait until Kate makes up her mind. And rest assured, my dear, that once Katie Drexel makes up her mind about her life's work, you will probably be the first to know. Don't rush her. There's plenty of time.

"Now," he commanded playfully, "please let your sleepy husband get some rest. And you go to sleep, too."

Emma Drexel did not go to sleep. *I only wish I, too, believed there was plenty of time,* she thought. *He's so right, though. Elizabeth will marry, and Louise will never be lonely regardless of what she decides to do. I must pray that God may help me to understand what He wants of Kate.*

By the fall of 1881, it was apparent that Johanna had not been far wrong in saying that Mrs. Drexel did not look well. Even Elizabeth and Louise had to admit that their mother's health seemed to be failing. All three of the girls tried to relieve her of household duties and cares, but it was Kate who appeared with a glass of water when her mother felt suddenly thirsty, or placed a dish of fruit on the table closest to her bed on evenings when Mrs. Drexel had scarcely touched her dinner.

Francis Drexel called in the best doctors available, and, by the spring of the following year, his wife seemed better. The family returned to St. Michel, where they stayed through the fall and into the early winter. Mrs. Drexel was beginning to take an interest in household affairs again. In December she surprised the family by deciding that they would not spend Christmas in the country.

"It's been so long," she said dreamily, "since we passed a Christmas at 1503. Joe and Miss Cassidy can go in early and make sure the house is ready. We will follow in the carriage, and when we get there, the house will be all aglow with lights. The wreaths at the windows will add a holiday touch, and your father will be at the organ. I do hope he will play some Christmas music for me."

The family arrived at their Walnut Street house five days before Christmas. Emma Drexel's every wish had been granted, and, as she smiled on them, her husband and her children told themselves that this was one of many happy Christmases to come.

Their joy continued to mount when, near the end of January, Mama went for a drive through the city she loved so much. Their joy was soon to end, though, for less than a week after the drive Emma Bouvier Drexel died. A Requiem Mass was offered at St. Mary's, and she was laid to rest in the Bouvier vault in St. Mary's Churchyard.

Louise and Elizabeth seemed to cling to each other in their sorrow, but Kate sat with her father through the first weeks. Together they read the obituaries from papers published all over the country. Though Kate knew about most of her mother's charities, she was amazed to learn that more than 150 poor families depended upon Emma Drexel to pay their rent. It was estimated, she read, that this "Lady Bountiful" distributed over $20,000 each year among the needy of her native Philadelphia.

Despite their sorrow, it was soon apparent to everybody in Kate's family that Emma Drexel's death had wrought a remarkable change in Elizabeth. Almost overnight she seemed to step into her mother's place, and the comfort of each member of the family became her chief concern. All social activities were pushed aside, and, as soon as possible, Elizabeth moved the family back to St. Michel in order to escape scenes connected with the death of their loved one.

As the flowers blossomed on the grounds of St. Michel, there was gradually heard the happy laughter which had once meant that the Drexels were at home. Louise spent most of her days outdoors with her dogs, or riding with Kate and Elizabeth. Francis Drexel spent his days at the bank, but faced an empty place at the end of the table when he sat down to dinner with the girls. By the end of the summer, he decided that a trip to Europe would dull the edge of their grief. Little did Francis Drexel realize the effect this trip would have on the life of one of his girls.

Chapter Six

A Vision

KATE and her sisters were grateful for the warm affection with which Johanna and Miss Cassidy surrounded them after their mother's death. Since Johanna had gone on the first European trip, Francis Drexel spoke about taking Miss Cassidy on the second jaunt. Louise and Elizabeth were delighted at the prospect of Miss Cassidy's going, but Kate, for some reason, showed little enthusiasm.

"You don't seem a bit happy that Miss Cassidy is

going," Elizabeth told Kate. "Don't you think she deserves to go somewhere sometime? She's always the one who is left behind."

"Maybe Kate's afraid there won't be anybody to whom she can write those long letters if Miss Cass is with us," Louise said, watching Kate's reaction.

"If you want to know," Kate began, "I'm not sure Mama would have placed so much responsibility on Joe, though I am sure she would have wanted Miss Cassidy to have the trip. Joe has the best heart in the world, but we all know that there are times when she can be very highhanded with the servants. You know how Mama felt about that, and we must try to carry out her wishes."

"Leave it to Kate to see the practical side of the matter," Elizabeth sighed. "I guess we *were* thinking more of our own pleasure. If Joe should happen to fling one of her temperamental fits . . ."

"We just might come home to two houses and a farm—minus any servants except one Johanna Ryan," Louise agreed.

"Oh, it might not be that bad," Kate laughed.

"Kate's right," Elizabeth said. "I'll ask Papa to book passage for Joe and to ask Miss Cassidy if she will consent to act as a sort of general manager of home affairs. How does that sound?"

The Drexels sailed on the S.S. *Scythia* in early October of 1883. Francis Drexel and Joe were the only able-bodied sailors among them for the first two days, but after Joe and the cabin boy forced the girls to drink the juice of two lemons, Kate and Louise rallied enough to take part in shipboard activities.

"We went around recommending lemon juice to the bilious-faced passengers stretched out on steamer chairs," Kate wrote, "and had the satisfaction of putting two patients on their legs—but Elizabeth was not of that number."

The other passengers recognized the Drexels and, having read of their recent sorrow, made special efforts to be friendly.

Kate, now twenty-five, knew that Miss Cassidy and Joe had shared her mother's concern over her lack of interest in suitors, so she made sure that her letters to Miss Cassidy contained a description of all the young men she met aboard the *Scythia*. Yet there are times, Kate thought as she finished one of those letters, when I think she knows—almost better than anyone except Mama and Father O'Connor—that I could never find happiness in a life devoted to social pleasure.

When they landed in England, Kate and her

sisters reminded their father not to chance another visit to Westminster Abbey with Johanna. After a short trip to Chester, they went on to Dover and from there to Brussels, Antwerp, Amsterdam, and The Hague. Then came Nuremberg, Munich, and Venice.

Though thoughts of their mother were constantly with all of the girls, Kate seemed to find it easiest to speak of Mama when she was with her father. Francis Drexel had noticed that it was Kate who made arrangements for Masses when they visited churches first seen with their mother. It was also Kate who directed Miss Cassidy to send a check of ten dollars each month to Aunt Louise for a Mass offering.

Often when the girls went to an early Mass in Venice they came out of the church to find their father feeding the pigeons on the piazza of St. Mark's. One morning, after Louise and Elizabeth walked toward the hotel, Kate remained with her father. He spoke of his love for animals—dogs, horses, and the "little feathered things."

"St. Francis loved them, too," Kate murmured, half to herself.

"But it is for his love of the poor that you admire

the saint of Assisi, isn't it, Kate?" her father asked quietly.

"That came later," she admitted. "It was Francis, the gay troubadour, who interested us all when we were children and Mama used to read to us about him."

"Kate, your mother had a dream about you not too long before . . ."

"She wrote us about it." The girl winced at the sadness in her father's voice. "She said it was such a beautiful dream and so real."

"Yes, but I blame myself for not paying more attention to what she said that night."

"Why, Papa?"

"I think she knew she was going to die, Kate. And she was worried about you."

"But she told us she was worried because she couldn't understand the dream and because Elizabeth had laughed at my interpretation," Kate remembered. "Why was she worried about me, Papa?"

"I'm not sure." Francis Drexel placed a hand on his daughter's arm. "You will perhaps understand that better than your father. Let's go into church and ask her to intercede for us so that we may become resigned to this separation and that you may understand whatever divine Providence wills you to do."

Kate knelt in a pew facing the Madonna of San Marco. She thought of the dream her father had mentioned. If only I could talk to Mama now, she thought. There *is* something I must do—but I'm not sure what it is.

Kate looked at the little Madonna whose eyes were resting on the Infant. "Holy Mother," she prayed, "help me to do the will of your divine Son. I have no mother but you from whom I may seek counsel."

Suddenly it was as if the sun had burst through the clouds which had overshadowed the early hours of the day and found its way to the window nearest the statue. The light which played around the face of the Madonna was almost blinding. Then it softened, and the face Kate saw seemed to be the face of her mother. The girl turned toward her father, whose head was bowed in reverent prayer, but the statue frowned and Kate stayed the hand she had raised. Instead, she rose quietly and walked quickly to the foot of the statue. Once more the face wore a smile and the lips parted as if waiting to speak.

"What is it you want to tell me?" Kate asked.

"Freely have you received; freely give," said a

voice which was so soft Kate was forced to strain to hear each word.

"Mother—that's the gospel from which Francis took his Rule," Kate whispered. Then the statue was dark again—except for the reflection from the candles—and the face of the Madonna was as it had been when Kate first entered the church.

She looked around to make sure she was not dreaming. An altar boy came out of the sacristy with a lighted taper and walked toward the main altar. Mass was about to begin, and Kate returned to her father.

Before she could collect her thoughts, a hand was in front of her. In the hand was a picture of the little Madonna before whom she had just knelt. Kate looked up into the face of an attendant. The man impatiently pushed the card at her, handed one to Mr. Drexel, and continued to pass them out to the faithful who were gathering for this late Mass.

All during Mass Kate kept remembering the words, "Freely have you received; freely give." She wanted so much to tell her father about it, but she remembered the frown on the Madonna's face when she had raised her hand to touch him. Later, after they returned to the hotel, she wanted to talk to Elizabeth about the vision—for she was satisfied that was what it had been. Each time she felt so inclined, she remembered her mother's dream and that Elizabeth had described her interpretation as nonsense. That night her father handed Kate a letter from Bishop O'Connor. She realized suddenly that this was an experience she could discuss only with her spiritual director.

It was late that night when Kate finished the letter to the bishop. Then she wrote the date—November 18, 1883—on the little picture card of the Madonna at whose feet she had received a part of St. Francis' Rule. She vowed this Rule would become her way of life, too.

I'll keep this forever, she thought, placing the picture in her missal. The only trouble is that I still don't know *how* I am to give of what I have. If I am just to continue with the Dorcas, Mama would have said so. Surely they—my mother and His—will help me to find the way.

The Drexels made a pilgrimage to Padua where they begged the intercession of St. Anthony on behalf of Aunt Elizabeth who had shopped for baby Louise so many years before and who was now seriously ill. They reached Rome in time to celebrate Christmas.

On Christmas Eve they attended Mass in the sacristy of Santa Maria Maggiore, where five boards from the manger in which the Infant Jesus had lain the first Christmas in Bethlehem were exposed for veneration. Kate felt very close to our Lady and her Son in the presence of this relic. In an effort to be patient, she reminded herself of the years Jesus was subject to His parents' will.

The Drexels met two priests soon after they reached Rome. The acquaintance seemed only casual then, but these two priests were destined seriously to affect the lives of the Drexels. One was the Most Reverend John Seghers, bishop of Vancouver Island, known as the Apostle of Alaska. The other was Father Hylebos, a Belgian who had taken up missionary work in the northwestern part of the United States.

In the meetings which followed, Bishop Seghers told many interesting stories of his work among the Eskimos, but Kate was enchanted by Father Hylebos' accounts of his travels over Indian territory. The priests and the Drexels parted with little thought of meeting again.

It was only a few days after Christmas that the Drexels received permission to be present at a private Mass said by the Holy Father. Joe, whose health had prevented her from taking part in many of the activities during the trip, solemnly promised to control herself, and the family was received by His Holiness after Mass. The pontiff bestowed his blessing upon the faithful Philadelphians and sent a blessing to their friends and relatives in America.

As Kate knelt at the feet of the pope, she dared to raise her head and look into his eyes. The kindness she saw there gave her courage. A great feeling of peace came over her.

If only, she thought, I could talk with him privately. I am sure he could tell me what to do. Somehow I feel he has the key which will unlock the door for me. I must find a way to talk with him—perhaps not today—but I must, I must!

The memory of the sight of Pope Leo XIII so absorbed Kate that she barely heard her father when he told the girls, as they packed to leave Rome, that he had a surprise for Kate. Only after he mentioned a visit to Siena did Kate push aside her own thoughts. At last she was going to visit the home of her patron saint!

It was a frosty morning when the Drexel family reached Siena and walked down Dyers Street to the house where St. Catherine had lived. Inside, an altar had been built over the chimney in the kitchen.

"It's almost as if she could come into this room, push the chimney aside, and start to cook," Elizabeth murmured.

"I'd much prefer a fire that would give out some heat," Louise whispered back, shivering.

Kate wandered into Catherine's tiny bedroom. Everything was unchanged. The smell of ill-tanned leather was still present, and Kate remembered that Catherine had been the child of a prosperous wool dyer. When the rest of the family visited the little chapel which had been built over a part of the house and the garden, Kate remained in the cell-like bedroom.

"Please, dear Catherine," she whispered as she knelt in the spot where the saint had slept on her board-bed, "beg our divine Lord to give me the spiritual enlightenment to give freely so that those with whom I share shall proclaim the greater honor and glory of God."

On the Drexels went, and the first anniversary of Emma Drexel's death was only a day or so away when they reached San Remo. They had intended to have Mrs. Drexel's anniversary Mass said at Lourdes, but with the time so near, they remained in San Remo to commemorate the anniversary.

It was the first of February when Joe, the girls, and their father arrived in Lourdes. After four hard-on-the-knees days during which they prayed in the grotto, drank the water, kissed the ground, lit the candles, and bathed in the miraculous water of the spring, the girls were completely awed by the spiritual atmosphere of Lourdes.

"It's almost like being in another world," Kate mused. "The Hotel de la Grotte might just as well be on another planet."

"I don't think I even laughed," Louise admitted, "until the Duke of Norfolk and his party came."

"Wasn't it funny when we first heard Miss Stadpole say, 'My papa, the priest?' " Elizabeth recalled.

The Duke of Norfolk had arrived at the hotel some time before. In his party was a Catholic priest and a young woman, Miss Stadpole, with her aunt. Kate and her sisters made the acquaintance of Miss Stadpole and, in the course of conversation, they learned that the priest was her father. They later learned that Monsignor Stadpole was a convert who had been ordained after the death of his wife. But the Drexel girls never forgot their astonishment when Miss Stadpole first referred to her "papa, the priest."

It was Lent when the Drexels reached Paris, and, by Eastertime, they were in London. Johanna's grief over the loss of Mrs. Drexel was still strong, and the girls began to feel that the trip had been too strenuous for her. They were glad to sail for home at the end of April.

Soon after they reached the States, Aunt Elizabeth died—an added sorrow for Kate and her sisters. They almost dreaded going back to St. Michel, though they were glad to be among familiar scenes again. They watched their father the first night as he walked from room to room.

"It's almost as if he expects to find Mama hiding in some secret corner," Kate told her sisters.

In an effort to create a cheerful atmosphere, Miss Cassidy had had flowers placed throughout the house, but even this reminded the family of the loved one who had planted most of the flowers.

In spite of her protracted mourning, it was "good old Joe" who made the girls push aside their own grief. "Mr. Drexel isn't looking his usual self," she told them one evening as they sat on the porch waiting for their father to return from the city. "Ever since we've been back he's been restless. He isn't eating well, either."

"That might be my fault," Elizabeth spoke up. "I haven't spent as much time as I might on the weekly menu. But I'll try to do better and see if I can remember all of Mama's favorite dishes."

"I'll have to start our walks again," Louise decided. "I guess we were so busy thinking about ourselves we forgot how lonely it has been for Papa."

Kate thought a moment before she spoke. "I'll have him set up a housekeeping account for me," she said. "Then I can relieve him of taking care of household bills."

"At least you didn't bite my head off," Joe snorted as she rose and walked toward the door. "A body never knows what to say these days."

"We're really very grateful to you, Joe," Kate replied, smiling, "for reminding us of how blind we've been."

"It's been hard on me, too." Joe stood in the doorway with her back to Kate and her sisters. "She—she was just like a sister to me." With a cry Louise ran to the older woman who was openly sobbing by that time.

In the distance Kate heard the crunch of carriage wheels on the driveway.

"Take them upstairs," she told her older sister. "It will never do for Papa to see both of them cry-ing. This is just the kind of scene which will make him feel worse."

Kate breathed a sigh of relief when her father greeted her. He was so cheerful that she was curious. When he kissed her on each cheek she spoke up.

"Remember you and Mama used to tell us how the Bouvier kin kissed you on both cheeks the first time you went to Pont St. Esprit?"

"What a memory my Kate has." Her father laughed. "But I have good news tonight, and there will be special kisses for all of my girls. Where's the rest of the family?"

"They're late dressing. They'll be down by the time you're ready for dinner," Kate said.

Francis Drexel chuckled as the girls plied him with questions about his good news. "It might spoil your dinner," he teased. "Wait till after dessert."

It was not until the table had been cleared that Mr. Drexel told them, "We're going out West—all the way to Portland, Oregon. And we'll make a detour so you can see Yellowstone National Park."

"Will we be going through Indian territory?" Kate asked. "Remember the stories Father Hylebos told us in Rome about his work among the Indians?"

"We certainly will pass through Indian territory.

Do you think three city-bred girls will enjoy such a trip?"

"Will we?" Louise's eyes were dancing. "And I'm going to get the best Indian pony I can find and ride all over the mountains."

"You won't have to worry about the mountains," her father laughed. "We'll be traveling in a special railroad car, the *Yellowstone*. It belongs to J. J. Hill, president of the Northern Pacific Railroad—and he's putting it at our disposal for the duration of the trip."

"I still want a pony," Louise insisted. "All my life I've wanted an Indian pony."

"And all *my* life I've wanted to see a real Indian village," Kate admitted, as Francis Drexel continued to chuckle over their excitement.

Chapter Seven

Of Bandits and Indians

IT was our Lady's birthday—September 8, 1884—
when Kate and her sisters left St. Michel on the most
adventuresome trip of their lives. After Mass and
Holy Communion at Eden Hall, the girls and their
father drove into the city. Here they were joined
by Mary Dixon, daughter of Aunt Elizabeth, whose
recent death had so grieved them, and two young

men from the Drexel firm. The richly furnished *Yellowstone* stood on a sidetrack waiting for the Drexels and for the engine which would start them on their journey westward.

Kate's intense interest in Father Hylebos' Indian missions had not escaped her father. Perhaps, he thought, this is a key to the vocation she is seeking. When Drexel & Company began to consider investing in the Northern Pacific Railroad, Francis Drexel knew he would have to make a trip to the West. It could, he hoped, serve a practical, as well as a pleasant, purpose.

As the train sped westward, Papa Drexel crossed off the days of the week. Gardiner, Montana, was to be the first stop. The conductor had assured Mr. Drexel they would reach that town on Saturday night so that they could hear Mass Sunday morning. One of the railroad officials had arranged to meet them there.

The *Yellowstone* was sidetracked, however, and missed connections. When Francis Drexel learned that they might not reach Gardiner before Sunday afternoon, he demanded that the *Yellowstone* be stopped at Bismarck, North Dakota. A telegram was sent to Gardiner, advising J. J. Hill's agent of the change.

The Drexel party attended an early Mass at Bismarck. When they returned to the *Yellowstone*, they were told that it would be several hours before the car would be picked up by the engine that would take them on to Gardiner. The girls wanted to stretch their legs, so back to church they went.

"I had so hoped," Kate told her father later, "that the sermon would bring some consolation to Mary Dixon. Her sorrow over the loss of dear Aunt Elizabeth seems to hang over all of us whenever there's a lull. Instead, the priest spoke on 'The Neglect of Parents in Educating Boys'—a likely subject for four young unmarried ladies!'"

The delay stretched into hours. The *Yellowstone* was switched around until it was on the main track and an engine finally picked it up. The party retired for the night, knowing that the *Yellowstone* would be approaching Gardiner, Montana, when they awakened.

The girls found their father anxiously consulting his watch when they joined him and the young men from his office early the next morning.

"We're pulling into Gardiner now," he explained, "but we're twelve hours late. I was to meet one of J. J. Hill's men here. That's why I sent the telegram ahead, but I mentioned only a six-hour delay."

When the conductor came to the door of the *Yellowstone* to tell them that they would be in Gardiner in five minutes, the girls gathered on the observation platform at the rear of the car.

As the train pulled into the station, they noticed an unusually large crowd of people standing around. "What's all the excitement?" the girls heard the conductor call to one of the trackmen.

"Ain't sure yet," the man answered, "but it looks as if the bandits are riding again."

"I think we'd better go inside," Kate suggested, and the girls went in to tell Papa what they had heard.

Before Mr. Drexel could leave the *Yellowstone*, an excited young man appeared. He was so busy mopping his red face that he collided with Mr. Drexel in the doorway. "Are you Mr. Francis A. Drexel?" he asked.

"I am." Francis Drexel bowed. "And who, may I ask, are you?"

"Mr. Drexel, I've never been happier to see anybody in my life. Mr. Hill instructed me to meet you, and I got your telegram Saturday. You said you would be here last night and that you would wire later—but I never heard another thing—and then, after all the excitement . . ."

"Pardon me," Mr. Drexel interrupted, "but what is all the excitement about?"

"Oh—you didn't know?" the man exclaimed. "It seems that word got around that a party of rich Eastern bankers was coming, and some outlaws who have been hiding out near here suddenly appeared in town. Somehow they knew your train was due here last night. About thirty minutes before you were expected, they came here to the station and pulled their guns on the stationmaster. He thought it was just a holdup and tried to fight them."

"But we sent another message saying we'd be delayed still more."

"That I never got, Mr. Drexel. You see, the stationmaster is also the telegraph clerk, and he's still in bad shape—much worse than I am." The man removed his hat to show a lump on his forehead.

"What happened to you?" Mr. Drexel was alarmed.

"When I came down to meet you, I went inside to see if there was a message for me. They grabbed me as soon as I stepped inside the door. They had bound and gagged the stationmaster. When I tried to get away, something hit me over the head. I don't remember anything else—but a brakeman found both of us tied up when he came on duty this morning."

Francis Drexel turned to his daughters. "Perhaps you didn't enjoy the sermon in Bismarck," he told them, "but if you hadn't stayed and gone to that second Mass, we might all be dead. Worse still, they might have let some of us go and held you girls for ransom."

After the narrow escape at Gardiner, the Drexels went on through Idaho and into Washington Territory. They stopped at Tacoma, then only a struggling village.

Kate thought often of the little Madonna of San Marco and of her experience at the feet of the statue. She had been disappointed in Bishop O'Connor's reaction. He had insisted that she was not ready to begin her life's work, whatever it was to be. Everything that had or was happening, he said, was preparation. Kate was reminded of this by a pleasant surprise in Tacoma.

When she had asked where they might find a Catholic church, the maid in the hotel had pointed to a tiny building perched on one of the hills. With their cousin, Mary, the girls climbed the hill early the following morning. They stopped at the modest

ectory next to the church to inquire the hour of the
next Mass.

Kate ran ahead and rang the doorbell while the
other girls stood on the hillside admiring the scenery.
As the door was opened, she stood stunned, staring
at the priest in front of her. This can't be the priest
we met in Rome, she thought. Of all the missions in
the Northwest, this couldn't possibly be Father
Hylebos' church!

Father Hylebos' greeting removed all doubt.

"To what do I owe the pleasure of having Miss
Drexel of Philadelphia call on me?" he laughed.
"Oh, I should say the Misses Drexel," he added as
the other girls joined them.

"Kate," Elizabeth demanded after the excitement
had died down, "are you sure you didn't know
Father Hylebos was here? Maybe *this* is where you
planned to see the Indian village."

They all laughed, and Kate insisted she had had
no idea that Father Hylebos was in Tacoma.

"Why, I expected to greet some women's rights
delegation," the priest laughed, "and to be bom-
barded with petitions to help further the cause of the
franchise for women. Instead, I see the charming
friends I made in Rome last year . . ."

Kate's father had made plans for that day, and the

Yellowstone was scheduled to leave Tacoma the following afternoon, but it was agreed that the girls would attend an early Mass at Father Hylebos' church the next morning.

"Then I will drive you out into the forest to see one of my missions—that is, if the mission hasn't moved," he added.

"What do you mean, Father?" Kate asked.

"The Indians move their villages according to the work they are doing," he explained. "We will go out to Puyallup and, as they say in Philadelphia, hope for luck."

Luck was not with the Philadelphians, however, and, when they reached what had been an Indian village, it looked like only a deserted meadow to Kate and her sisters.

As they turned away, Father Hylebos saw an old Indian man with a small boy resting by the roadside. "Where?" the priest asked, pointing to the deserted village.

"Hops—hop fields," the old man replied.

"Are you going, too?" the priest asked.

"Ugh!" The old man grunted and bowed his head several times before he pulled the child to its feet and walked in the direction of the hop fields to which he had pointed.

"They are harvesting the hops," the priest explained. "They will camp as near to the fields as
possible. It would be, perhaps, a two-hour drive
with these weary old horses pulling us and the carriage."

"Father," Elizabeth asked, "do you mean that
old man is going to walk the distance it would take
the horses two hours to cover?"

"And what about the little boy?" Kate put in.
"Perhaps we could make room for them in the carriage."

"He would not ride with you," the priest explained. "I do not know whether he was left behind
or returned for some forgotten object. But he will
join his people. And the child—it is perhaps his
grandson—will be proud that his grandfather is so
swift of foot."

The girls agreed that there was not time enough
for them to risk a drive deeper into the forest, so
they returned to the rectory. Kate had noticed the
bareness of the church and wondered how she
could help without offending the priest. When
Father Hylebos left them alone, the girls held a conference, each expressing a desire to help. Francis
Drexel had recently opened bank accounts for his
daughters, and they had generous monthly allow-

ances which they were free to spend as they wished

"If you don't mind," Kate told her sisters, "I'd
like to take Father Hylebos' work as my special
charity—like Mama's Dorcas. I've always been interested in the Indians. They've had to suffer so
many injustices. This way I'll feel that I am sharing
what I have with them."

When Kate spoke to Father Hylebos, he was
delighted with her offer of help. "I remember your
devotion to our Lady," he said, "and we do not yet
have a statue. That would be a most welcome gift.
The Indians have great love for the mother of our
Lord."

Kate selected a statue from a catalogue Father
Hylebos gave her, but she hesitated a moment before she wrote the check. She thought of the little
Madonna in Venice and the words "Freely have you
received; freely give." The statue would cost $100
and Kate was afraid her father would think her
extravagant. Then she remembered St. Francis, and
how he had incurred the wrath of his father to
"freely give." Kate Drexel wrote her first check
with conviction and pride and thrilled to the sin-
cerity of Father Hylebos' "God bless you, my
child!"

That evening, after the *Yellowstone* was on the

way to Kalama, from which point they were to go by boat to Portland, Kate told her father about the statue.

"I was afraid you would think me extravagant," she admitted.

"My dear Kate," he said, placing a hand on her shoulder with affection and feeling, "I am glad you did this."

That night Kate slept peacefully, except for a pleasant dream. Once more she was talking about the statue to her father, and, as he expressed his approval, her mother joined them, smiling as she said, "This is the beginning." Even in her sleep Kate seemed to know she was dreaming, but the slumber which followed was deep and refreshing. When they reached Kalama the next day, she felt as if life—a glorious life—were just beginning.

As the Portland-bound boat pulled away from the shore, Kate's sisters and Mary Dixon commented on her high spirits and flushed cheeks.

"It must be the spirit of the wild and woolly West," Louise said. "I don't know when I have seen Kate look so happy."

Kate's father was standing beside her as she leaned against the rail of the deck. "It's our secret, isn't it?" he asked.

"Secret? I'm not sure I understand what you mean, Papa."

"The spirit of giving, Kate. And the happiness it gives you. I hope God always grants you the wisdom to use what you have as well as you did in Tacoma."

A gathering mist dampened the deck, and the rest of the party went indoors. Kate and her father remained where they were, watching the land slide away, each filled with an abiding love of God, family, and the vast country they were exploring.

Chapter Eight

A Door Is Closed

MARY Ann Cassidy was delighted with the account the three Drexel girls gave of their western trip. On the rare occasions when she exchanged confidences with Johanna, she was apt to refer to the pleasant lines along which her life had fallen. Since the death of her mother, she had lived with the Drexels.

"Few teachers," she said, "have had the opportunity of seeing their pupils develop day by day—

then year by year—as has been my lot. Sometimes when I go to the old classroom—now a classroom no longer—it is hard for me to realize that they are grown. Just think of it, my petite Louise is twenty-two years old."

"Elizabeth is thirty, and it's twenty-seven that Kate will be in November," Johanna reminded. "It's high time Elizabeth and Louise were thinking about families of their own, though I don't think Kate will ever leave her father—not unless something happens to convince her that her life's work is elsewhere."

"You know our Kate," Miss Cassidy smiled. "She was never one to jump at quick decisions, but once she has arrived at a conclusion—and her thinking is almost always sound—she cannot easily be swayed. I know her well enough to see that there is something—some course of action—she is weighing now. I've noticed it ever since her mother's death."

Johanna tiptoed to the door and closed it. "I've an idea," she whispered, "that Kate's just waiting for Bishop O'Connor. I don't think it will be so long now before we know what she's going to do."

"I'm not too sure it is only Bishop O'Connor's blessing she is waiting on." Kate's teacher thought for a while. "There's some indecision—I don't know what—but it's there. I do know she is not interested in any of the young men who come here, though I can't say the same for Elizabeth and Louise."

"Kate seems taken with the idea of helping that priest we met in Rome who works with the Indians out West." Johanna shook her head. "What with the robbers and bad food, I'd be just as happy if she forgot about the good father and his Indians."

Miss Cassidy laughed. "Kate is not one to change easily. She's started a correspondence with him already, and I can tell from the letter she showed me that she plans to set aside a portion of her allowance for his missions."

Miss Cassidy was right. Kate had decided to set aside a part of her allowance each month for the Indian missions. She shared Father Hylebos' dream of the day when there would be a school at Tacoma where children from the Yakima, Tulipup, Puyallup, and Nesqually tribes might be taught reading, writing, and religion.

As Christmas approached, Kate and her sisters busied themselves with preparations for the disposal of gifts of food, clothing, and money through the Dorcas.

"Do you think this is the way Mama would have done it?" was a question they often asked each other when checking over the list of families who were to receive help and deciding on the form this help should take.

A few days before Christmas the girls received a partial answer to their question. Johanna, who had always assisted Emma Drexel with the Dorcas, inspected with a critical eye the work the girls had done.

"Your own dear mother could not have done better," she said, "though she might have saved a penny here and there. You'll learn, though."

The girls laughed when Johanna left the room because it was a standing joke that their friend was wary of paying compliments.

It was a quiet family Christmas, and on January 29 the girls and their father attended a second anniversary Mass for Mrs. Drexel. As they approached the communion rail, Kate thought about the little Virgin of San Marco and was pleased that her father was kneeling beside her when she begged her two mothers to smile upon their child.

Two days after the anniversary, Francis Drexel told his daughters he wanted to go out to St. Michel. The weather was cold, but clear, and the girls enjoyed the ride out to Torresdale. Their father was exceptionally quiet as they reminisced and pointed out familiar scenes. Occasionally he smiled at some happy memory, but later they reminded each other that he had been pensive throughout the journey.

After lunch, Louise, who was her father's favorite walking companion, coaxed him into making a short tour of the grounds. Kate insisted that he wear a muffler and personally buttoned his greatcoat at the neck. When Elizabeth made as if to help her father with his gloves, he pushed her aside playfully.

"Anybody would think I was an invalid," he laughed, "to see you girls fussing over me."

"I'd rather think," Kate said with feeling, "that they would know you were a very special father."

A slight drizzle had begun before Francis Drexel and Louise returned, but they changed their clothes immediately and rejoined Elizabeth and Kate to bring them up to date on barnyard happenings.

The next day—Sunday, February 1, 1885—the Drexels returned to the city. Dinner was served in the early afternoon, and Louise and her father decided they would finish the walk which had been interrupted by rain the day before. The next morning Papa appeared to have a slight cold. Two days later, the doctor told the girls their father had a mild case of pleurisy. They were also told that there was no immediate danger, but Francis Drexel was an important figure in the economy of his country and the doctors took every precaution. Elizabeth received their orders as to treatment, diet, and medication, and then divided other sickroom duties with Kate, who had appointed herself nurse.

Francis Drexel submitted to the ministrations of the girls and, ten days later, was allowed to leave his bed. Kate selected several books from the Drexel library and placed them on a table near her father's favorite chair.

Though Miss Cassidy had continued her duties as a sort of general manager, she often found herself cast in the old role of teacher, as well. Her opinion on books, plays, and current events was respected by all of the girls, and on Lincoln's birthday, 1885, over a late lunch with Kate, she was discussing the merits of "Old Abe," both as President and as Great Emancipator. Suddenly they heard the organ. At first the music was so soft they both thought they were imagining it. Then a swell of beautiful notes seemed to echo throughout the house.

"He must be better," Miss Cassidy murmured, surprised. "I haven't heard such a joyful note in his music since your mother's death, and there's strength there, too. He isn't simply touching the keys."

"There's strength in the pedal movements, too," Kate said, and alarm began to show in her face. "The doctors want him to be quiet and avoid any exertion. As happy as I am to hear the music again, for I know how much the organ means to him, we cannot risk a setback. We'd better take him back to his room."

Kate jumped up, but Mary Ann Cassidy did not. "You're anxious, of course, Kate dear," she said quietly, as she gently drew the girl down again, "but you know that neither of us would dare to interrupt your father when he is at his organ. Wait until the music stops; then help him to his room."

"You're right," Kate admitted. "Now that Papa is out of danger, I should be less anxious, but I'm so afraid something might happen to him. If he died—I think I should die, too!"

"Kate Drexel!" Miss Cassidy rose and faced her former pupil. "I'm surprised at you! Don't forget that your father has been very lonely these past two years. And when you're older, you'll understand that there are many things worse than dying. Loneliness is said to be one of them."

"Papa always had us," Kate insisted, though she was secretly ashamed that her emotions had betrayed her.

"Have you ever thought that there must have

been times when he wondered whether Louise might have preferred being with that handsome young lawyer, Morrell, or that Elizabeth might have turned down invitations to accompany Walter George Smith and his sister to the theater?'' Miss Cassidy pressed her advantage. ''And he knows that one of the reasons—though I'm not saying it is the only one—you have not decided what you are going to do is because you are clinging to him.''

''How do you know all this?'' Kate asked. ''Did Papa ever tell you these things?''

''As time passes,'' Miss Cassidy said, smiling sadly, ''you come to understand the thoughts of those you love—even when they are not put into words. And, Kate, you and your family are very dear to me.''

''Oh, Miss Cass.'' Kate slipped into the greeting Louise sometimes used for their teacher. ''You are a *part* of us! Why, you are almost a Drexel. Nothing will ever separate us. And when Papa gets well, we are going to plan a trip and you are going with us. We'll go to Ireland with you; then we'll go to Assisi for me, and Elizabeth and Louise want to go to Spain. So we'll go there, too, and we'll come back to Rome. I'd like to have another audience with the pope. Oh—and we'll go to Annecy and see the house where Francis de Sales lived. He's Papa's patron saint, you know. We'll have one grand splurge and then . . ."

"And then what?"

"I will pray," Kate began, "that I may . . ."

The door was opened abruptly. "Where is Papa?" Elizabeth asked excitedly. "The moment we came in the house Louise and I both dropped our packages and ran up to his room, but he isn't there."

"We hadn't noticed that the music had stopped," Miss Cassidy said. "Your father has been at the organ. He's probably resting a bit before returning to his room."

"What a fright!" Elizabeth sank into a chair. "Shopping with Louise is no easy task and I really overstayed my time. Then, when I didn't find him— I didn't know what to think."

"He's most likely in his room now," Miss Cassidy said as Kate started up the stairs, "but I don't think you girls should let him see how anxious you are about him. Cheerfulness is important to a convalescent."

Kate was reluctant to leave her father alone after the incident on Lincoln's birthday. The following Sunday afternoon she watched him as he selected one of the books she had placed on his table, adjusted his eye glasses, and found the page he had marked.

After consulting the written directions Elizabeth had given her concerning medication for her father, Kate settled down to read until it was time for the patient's next dose. She had been reading for fifteen or twenty minutes when she looked up to find her father's eyes on her. He smiled, then removed his glasses and rose as if to walk toward her.

"Papa," Kate asked quickly, "is there anything you'd like me to get for you?"

But before his daughter could reach him, Francis Drexel had slumped back into his chair. Beads of perspiration lined his brow, and Kate saw a sightless stare in his eyes.

"Elizabeth! Louise! Call the doctor. I'm going to St. Patrick's for a priest," Kate screamed as she stopped in the hallway to grab a wrap.

Cutting through Rittenhouse Square, Kate ran as fast as she could. Bareheaded and with her open coat flapping in the wind, she was insensible to everything except her desire to get a priest to her father. She had seen death in his eyes; there was no need to hope. Panting, she ran up the steps of St. Patrick's rectory, pushed past the maid who opened the door, and rushed into the parlor where a group of priests was having a conference.

"Come quick!" she cried. "My father is dying!"

The stunned priests remained seated.

"My God!" Kate moaned. "My father is dying and they won't come."

One of the priests, Father Mulholland, who recognized Kate, rose quickly. "Yes, my child," he said calmly. "I shall come at once."

As through a veil, Kate saw the priest leave while other figures moved around her. She heard a familiar voice, and after a while recognized Mary Jane, one of the Drexel servants.

"Come with me, Miss Kate," the woman kept saying. "Come with me."

"Papa? How's my father?"

"I heard you talking to your sister," Mary Jane told her, "so I took a cab to St. John's and got a priest. The driver waited and I came over here for you."

One of the priests helped Kate to the cab and in a few minutes they were back at 1503 Walnut Street. Suddenly there was a flicker of hope, and Kate's legs, which seemed to have turned to rubber, were strong again. She ran up the steps to her father's room, then stopped on the threshold.

He was lying in bed, straight and still. His eyes were closed, and a man whose back was to Kate leaned over the inert form. Quickly she walked over to the bed. Then she knew that her father was dead.

Kate heard Louise, then Elizabeth, speak to her, but the room seemed to be filled with people whose faces she could not distinguish. She lost track of time and movement, but she knew they were talking about her when she heard a voice say, "She has gone into a state of shock."

Francis Anthony Drexel died on February 15. He was buried the following Thursday from St. Mary's Church, and his mortal remains were placed temporarily in the Bouvier vault at St. Mary's Churchyard.

Letters and telegrams of condolence were received by the Drexel sisters from all sections of the United States and Europe. Francis Drexel had made numerous friends through his own firm in Philadelphia, through Drexel, Morgan & Company in New York, and through Drexel, Harjes & Company in Paris. Though notables such as ex-President Grant and outstanding men from the literary, musical, and philanthropic fields mourned the passing of Kate's father, it was the poor whose grief touched the hearts of those he had left behind.

Men stood outside the church and bared their heads to a biting wind when the body was taken to the vault. Women who had never seen Francis Drexel in their lives wept without shame. They did not know that the friend they mourned had left the bulk of his vast fortune to God's needy. No one knew, or could know, of the heroic manner in which the good works begun by Francis Anthony Drexel and his wife, Emma, would go on and on.

Chapter Nine

The Key Is Found

THERE was a quiet determination on the part of the three Drexel sisters that life at 1503 Walnut Street should continue as their parents would have liked it. The Dorcas and all other charities were carried on with painstaking diligence. Especially were the girls concerned about the orphans, for their father's loving care of those unfortunate children was one of the dominating interests of his life. In his will, he had made liberal bequests to many orphanages, but the girls sought to continue his personal interest as well.

Elizabeth took the initiative in planning for future Drexel projects, while Louise contributed her boundless supply of energy. The shock of her father's death had left Kate's health so impaired that, in the early months of planning, she could give only her prayers.

Kate was almost sure that she should embrace the religious life, but she was not sure what order she should enter, or what special direction her life was to take. Bishop O'Connor continued to tell her to be patient when she asked, "How long?" Except for consoling letters from this wise spiritual director, the only bright spot in Kate's life was the pleasure she derived from helping Father Hylebos and his Indian missions.

More and more she yearned to talk with the man who was then called the Prisoner of the Vatican. The kindness and wisdom she had seen in the gentle smile of Leo XIII had kindled a great hope. Kate tried hard to rise above her personal problems, but she had lost interest in all else, and the more she struggled to reach a decision, the more her health suffered.

Since the death of his brother, Anthony J. Drexel

had thrown a protective arm around his three nieces, and it was after a conference with Uncle Anthony that Louise and Elizabeth approached Kate about the possibility of going to Europe again.

"I want to establish an industrial institution for orphan boys which will be a memorial to Papa," Elizabeth told Kate. "Uncle Anthony tells me there are many such institutions in Europe. We could learn how to conduct such a school, and then we could go to a health resort in Germany and you could take the baths."

"Oh, Kate, it would do you a world of good," Louise coaxed. "And Uncle Anthony knows just the spot. He says he's going there for a rest as soon as he feels they can spare him from the bank."

"I would like to go to Europe," Kate admitted, "but I'm not sure I feel up to it yet, and I hadn't thought of going to Germany."

"You've always wanted to go to Assisi." Louise could not conceal her eagerness. "And we could go there after you'd had the baths. We could even go to Rome again."

Perhaps, Kate thought, this is to be the answer to my prayers. She knew that her family was concerned about her health, and she hated to cause them added worry. "Where," she asked, "is the spot my kindest of uncles has recommended?"

"Schwalbach—between Eltzville and Wiesbaden," Louise said quickly, "and Dr. DaCosta knows a doctor there who will look after you. In a month's time my sister Kate will be as good as new!"

It was impossible for Kate to resist, and in a few moments all three of them were making plans for the trip.

Though the girls were anxious to complete plans for the establishment of the industrial school, it was months before a site was found which met the approval of their wise Uncle Anthony. Kate and Louise were pleased that the 200-acre tract which Elizabeth selected was at Eddington, not far from St. Michel. After much deliberation it was decided that the institution should be named St. Francis de Sales Industrial School in honor of the learned saint who had been their father's patron. With the help of their uncle, a general outline for the school had been put on paper and the plans for the building had been drawn before the girls started on their trip.

Miss Cassidy considered it her duty to remain at home while Kate and her sisters were away. She also recommended that Martin, the valet, should accompany the girls. "You have never traveled without the protection of a man," she said, "and I don't think your father would want you to do so now—especially with Kate's health being poor." Uncle Anthony seconded the recommendation and, as usual, Johanna was included in the party to chaperon and care for the special needs of the sisters. The party sailed for Europe on July 31, 1886.

The sea voyage was good for Kate, and, upon their arrival in Schwalbach, the Drexels sought out the doctor who had been recommended. Within a day or two the gentleman had familiarized himself with Kate's symptoms and she had begun the cure, which consisted of daily baths at the springs and a glass of water from the Weinbrunner Spring twice a day.

Schwalbach was situated in the heart of the Nassau hill and forest country. Quaint villages with picturesque walks and drives dotted the countryside. Johanna was always with Kate, whether she was at the baths or resting in the hotel. This gave Elizabeth and Louise a great deal of time to walk over hills, down dales, and through woods. There was hardly a village in the region that these two did not visit while Kate was, as she later said, luxuriating in mud baths and quaffing off cups that cure. After

five weeks the doctor dismissed the patient, who
reflected the effectiveness of his Schwalbach *kur*.

Kate and her sisters, with Johanna and Martin,
left Schwalbach and traveled southward through
the Rhine Valley. As they drove through the Black
Forest, an evening haze, spangled by flickering darts
of golden light, hung over the irregular ranges, and
Kate felt that her soul wanted to sing the praises of
the Creator Who had achieved such startling beauty.

Once more the Drexels stopped at Bern, but they
were not attracted to the great clock and its hourly
parade of animals as they had been twelve years before.

At Interlaken Kate felt the need to rest for a few
days and draw strength from the snow-capped
Jungfrau. Each morning as she knelt at Mass, she
offered prayers of thanksgiving. I know, she said
to herself over and over, that God has given us this
time of repose in order to form our plans.

One day in a foggy rain the girls made the ascent
to Murren, situated on a terrace over 5,000 feet
high. As they climbed higher and higher, Kate felt
a great joy. That night she set down in her journal
some of the reflections which had flooded her being as she stood poised halfway between heaven and
earth. "I felt as if standing at the Day of Judg-

ment," she wrote. "Man's life span is like the passing of a cloud over the unchanging mountains."

After visiting an industrial school at Geneva they went on to Annecy where St. Francis de Sales, patron of the school the Drexels would establish, had once lived.

Johanna had not been enthusiastic over the mountain-climbing trips which Kate and her sisters enjoyed, but she was always with them when they made pilgrimages. Kate was delighted that the old woman (for Joe of the fiery temper, quick tongue, and big heart was no longer young) enjoyed walking with them over the same streets that St. Francis de Sales had trod 300 years before.

They visited the church where Francis had preached—a large Gothic structure—and rang the front doorbell of the house where he had lived for twelve years. They also visited the chapel of the Visitation Convent, founded by St. Jane Frances de Chantal, the great woman who had been St. Francis de Sales' friend. As Kate knelt before the altar where the relics of her father's patron saint rested in a large marble sarcophagus, she could not help but wish that Papa could have been there.

Gold lamps hung around the side of the circular sanctuary. It was the custom to make an offering and have a light burned for a year before the saint's relics, the girls learned. Kate sought out the sacristan and gave him a fifty-franc note. "For the intentions and good health of all of my relatives and friends," she told him.

As Kate and her sisters left the church, Joe rushed in from the vestibule. "You might have told me those candles burn a year," she burst out. "You know Madame Moran would feel slighted if I passed up a chance to get a whole year of prayers for her." The girls smiled at Joe's thoughtfulness for Madame Moran, one of the Religious of the Sacred Heart at Eden Hall, whose friendship Johanna had cherished since her days as a novice.

Kate was not sure what she had thought would happen in Assisi. The sun shone brightly enough on the little town perched on the crest of a rocky hill where Francis Bernardone had grown up. The air was balmy, and she inhaled a certain fragrance as they rode past orange and olive groves. Almost as if in a dream, Kate heard her sisters comment on the beauty of the fruit and flowers which they passed, but her one desire was to go to the chapel of St. Mary of the Angels, the Portiuncula, where the son of wealthy Peter Bernardone had, through a revelation, learned what his way of life was to be.

The guide showed Kate and her sisters various places associated with the saint of Assisi. They were taken to the big beautiful church which had been built in his honor. Kate knelt before the relics and prayed, but even then she was distracted by the desire to reach the Portiuncula, Francis' "Little Portion." Elizabeth and Louise sensed Kate's impatience and, at the whispered urging of Joe, suggested that the party set out for the Portiuncula without delay.

Kate stood outside the Portiuncula for a moment and prayed that she, too, might be blessed with a revelation—that she might understand the special work God wished her to do. Through the Dorcas she had seen the suffering of God's poor. During the months the Drexels were at 1503, Elizabeth and two of her friends conducted a Sunday school for the Negro children at old St. Joseph's, and she talked often of their poverty. Every letter from Father Hylebos made Kate more aware of the need for schools and churches for the Indians. Two priests who were connected with the Bureau of Indian Affairs had visited the Drexels before they left home to beg support for the hundreds of these neglected Americans.

Yet what can I do to help them, Kate thought, when I am not sure what I must do with my own life? Then she remembered St. Francis' many attempts to go as a crusader to the Mohammedans of the East and how he later sent missionaries to Tunisia. Perhaps I can ask the Holy Father to send missionaries to the Indians, she thought, and she smiled, unaware that the miracle of grace was already working as she walked into the chapel where Francis had once knelt.

The revelation Kate had hoped for did not come in the way she had expected. While she knelt in the Portiuncula pondering the words of St. Matthew's Gospel, "Freely have you received; freely give," which had been accepted by Francis as his Rule, she knew only that she, who had freely received, must also freely give. A great impatience possessed her, and it seemed as if the birds outside the windows of the chapel were singing, "Rome! Rome! Rome!"

Kate's sisters were worried. They were afraid that the Assisi visit had been unsuccessful, that they had waited too long and that Kate had built up too many expectations. For the first time since the cure at Schwalbach their sister was listless and showed little interest in the food set before them at mealtime. Kate was silent on the trip to Rome, but Elizabeth and Louise kept reminding her that their old friend, Miss Carrere, was to meet them.

Kate's listlessness was of short duration, though, and when they reached Marseilles and their French teacher, Mademoiselle de St. Marsault, joined the party, Kate was as chatty as either of the other girls and said, "Do you remember when?" as many times as any of them.

It was like a homecoming when Kate and her sisters saw Miss Carrere—their beloved Caro—waiting for them at the station. Through various connections the request for an audience with Pope Leo XIII was made, and each day Kate hoped to receive word that permission for the audience with His Holiness had been granted.

It's almost like holding your breath, she thought one night when sleep was slow to come. This is what I have waited for, and yet, there is so much work to be done in this world I don't know where to start. I cannot be all things to all men. Yet I do not know which men are my special charge.

Kate and her sisters had found several stacks of

mail upon their arrival in Rome. The letters from Father Hylebos brought tears to Kate's eyes. There had been a drought and many of the Indians were starving. Other denominations were sending missionaries into his territory, and Kate detected a faint note of discouragement. Bishop O'Connor, in another letter, was already asking Kate if she felt free to share the result of her audience with the Holy Father. And each morning she faced a new day hopefully expecting to learn that tomorrow might be the one she had long awaited.

The summons finally came. On January 27, 1887, Kate and her party were granted the rare privilege of assisting at the Holy Mass celebrated by the pontiff. Afterward, they were to have a private audience with him. When Elizabeth and Louise reminded Joe to watch her behavior, Kate almost weakened in her determination to speak with the Holy Father about her vocation.

If, she thought, I could muster enough courage to tell him about Mama's dream and about what happened that day in Venice before the little Madonna of San Marco, I am sure he could tell me what it all meant.

Johanna checked the girls' black dresses and veils to make sure they were clothed according to reguation. When the carriage came, Kate was so excited she felt as if her knees would buckle. After they were shown into the chapel, she could hardly remember how they had gotten there. She kept wondering if anything would happen to keep the aging pontiff from celebrating that particular Mass or from granting them the promised audience. Her head was bowed when the holy celebrant approached the altar, but when she looked up and saw him, all her doubts and fears vanished. A calm which lasted throughout the Mass settled over Kate.

When they were ushered into the throne room, she was the one who appeared least nervous. Each of them knelt in turn to kiss the papal ring and to receive the blessing of their spiritual father. Then Elizabeth, as the eldest, asked the pope if he would send a blessing to their relatives and friends in America. It was at that point that Kate felt the Holy Father's eyes upon her. The friendliness in his glance gave her the courage she had prayed for.

I must tell His Holiness about the Indians and about the hardships Father Hylebos encounters in the Northwest, she thought. Then, if my courage lasts, I can speak of my own problems. Perhaps he will have an idea where my talents might be put to the best use.

Johanna could not resist the temptation to speak
of the many benefactions of Francis and Emma
Drexel and of how, since their death, the Drexel
girls were trying to carry on their parents' charities.
To the astonishment of her sisters, Kate then
stepped forward and proceeded to give a detailed
account of the sufferings of the American Indians
and of the hardships endured by priests who worked
with them. The pope leaned toward her as if to
hear better, and Kate felt she had captured his
interest.

"Your Holiness," she finished, "the Indians are
starving for spiritual, as well as material, food. Oh,
Holy Father, I beg you to send missionaries to
them."

The pope searched the face of the impassioned
girl who stood before him. Neither the wealth nor
the charity of the Drexels was unknown to him. For
a second he closed his eyes.

I've talked too much about the Indians, thought
Kate ruefully. I've tired him out and now I can't
ask him about my vocation.

As if he had read her thoughts, Leo XIII opened
his eyes, and the beauty of his smile seemed to wipe
out all trace of the many years which had bestowed
such great wisdom upon him. "Why," he said, "d

ou not become a missionary yourself, my child?"

The pope reminded Kate that she held within erself the ability to start a religious community for ork among the Indians. Here in Rome—the ternal City—at the feet of the supreme pontiff, she ad received her vocation.

Once more Kate knelt, this time to receive a lessing from the vicar of Christ who had opened ne door. The way—her life's work—lay straight head for Kate who had been christened Katharine Mary Drexel in the Church of the Assumption at hiladelphia, Pennsylvania, in the United States of young and vigorous America.

Chapter Ten

A Time for Parting

THOUGH the Drexels stopped at Paris and London before they sailed for America, Kate was already looking forward to a trip which would take her to the Northwest and to the Indians who were to be her children. She had written Bishop O'Connor about her audience with the Holy Father. "It seems," Kate told him, "that January 27, 1887, is the day for which I have waited all my life."

In spite of Kate's great joy, she warned her

sisters and Johanna not to mention her conversation with Pope Leo XIII. She feared the news might be spread, or be inaccurately reported, before her plans were complete.

Elizabeth and Louise were happy that Kate had found her vocation and, with the day of separation still indefinite, they brushed aside any thoughts of personal loss as being unworthy. Joe, too, was happy. Kate's vocation would, in a way, make up for her own disappointment over having to leave Eden Hall years before. Miss Cassidy, who had long suspected that Kate's vocation lay in the religious life, was relieved that the time of indecision was past.

Soon after they returned to St. Michel, Kate announced her intention to visit the Indians and her sisters promptly agreed to make the trip with her.

While the Drexels had been in Europe, the cornerstone for St. Francis de Sales Industrial School at Eddington had been laid. Now Elizabeth set about making plans for the dedication which was to take place within the next year.

Louise was busy with her own project. She had become interested in the new St. Joseph's Society, an order of priests devoted to the care of Negroes. While Kate was seeking advice from priests working with the Indians, Louise was familiarizing herself with the work of the Josephites.

Thus each of the three Drexel girls had found a channel through which she could share the worldly goods bequeathed by their generous father and their "Lady Bountiful" mother.

Kate knew that her work would cover a much broader area than Father Hylebos' missions and, on the advice of Bishop O'Connor, she sought out Bishop Martin Marty, O.S.B., then vicar apostolic of Northern Minnesota—later bishop of Sioux Falls, South Dakota—and Father Joseph A. Stephan, director of the Bureau of Catholic Indian Missions in Washington. The Drexel girls had already donated generously to these two priests.

From time to time collections for the Indians were taken up in the churches of Philadelphia, and among Kate's relatives and friends it became a standing joke that she would not allow one of them to escape. A fond relative once said that Kate's pocketbook was so heavy on the Sundays these collections were taken up that she had difficulty carrying it from the carriage to the church. He admitted, too, that he had allowed "the sweet benefactress" to empty his own pockets for her worthy cause.

Bishop Marty and Father Stephan were grateful for Kate's support and overjoyed when they learned from Bishop O'Connor that the Indian missions were to become her lifework. Pleased that the Drexels were agreeable to the idea of a trip which would entail certain hardships, Father Stephan hastened to invite them to visit Indian settlements in his territory.

They set out in mid-September, 1887, first to visit Bishop O'Connor in Omaha. The bishop was delighted with Kate's enthusiasm. She was approaching one of the biggest jobs any woman in her beloved America had ever taken upon herself, not realizing that she herself had been an answer to one of Bishop O'Connor's prayers.

He had long dreamed of a religious community of nuns to work among the Indians. Yet, as Kate talked of the great need of the "neglected and despised Indians" and of the shameful way they had been treated, the bishop reminded her that the Indians were not the only neglected and despised group; American Negroes shared this fate.

As he spoke, Kate recalled what Louise had once laughingly told her sister: "You have only some hundred thousand souls in your Indian field, but I have ten or more millions in my Negro harvest."

She also remembered a letter from Father Stephan in which he had told about confirmation at a church for Negroes in Washington. Father Stephan had been asked to celebrate the High Mass because, as he said, the "Blacks and Indians are color relations."

That's right, Kate thought now. They're color relations—all children of God who do not yet know His glory. From that time on she nursed the idea of including colored missions in her work.

After shopping for bright beads and gaily colored trinkets to give to the Indians, the Drexels began their tour with Bishop O'Connor and Father Stephan. They traveled part of the way by train and then set out on the open trail.

Elizabeth and Louise had brought their saddles, and they chose horses while Kate traveled in the carriage with Bishop O'Connor and Father Stephan.

Four miles from St. Francis Mission, Rosebud Agency, South Dakota, Kate and her sisters were thrilled by the colorful sight of six Indian police riding out to meet them. At the mission Father Stephan presented Bishop O'Connor and the Drexel sisters to Chief Roast-Big-Turkey. "How," probably a corruption of "How are you?", was the Indians' favorite greeting, and there was vigorous handshaking and much "howing." These members of the Sioux tribe were the first Indians the Drexels had ever spoken with.

Inspired though she was, Kate never lost her delightful sense of humor. Years later she was to recall laughingly their first night at an Indian mission. Father Stephan had neglected to tell the Sisters of St. Francis that he was bringing the bishop with a party of young ladies, and no preparations had been made for them. The mission had not been completed, but the nuns managed to improvise beds for the visitors on the first floor.

Uneasy and unable to sleep, the girls were grateful for the first signs of dawn. But when they started to get out of bed, they found that there were neither shades nor curtains at the windows. Pressed against the panes were several Indians' faces, their bright eyes peering at the strange palefaces. The nuns laughingly chased the Indians away and rescued the girls.

They attended Mass at the mission church, which was also incomplete. The benches were mere boards without backs, and the Indians treated these makeshift seats as playthings, stepping from one to the other like joyful children. Their glee was contagious, and Kate laughed out before she realized it.

"But I sobered quickly," she recalled later, "when the holy Jesuit reprimanded the Indians for want of reverence to the Blessed Sacrament."

After Mass there was a general "howing," followed by an ox feast. Kate and her sisters gave out gifts to the squaws in their brightly colored dresses and shawls, some with their faces painted, and most of them with papooses strapped to their backs. Some of the men were wrapped in unbleached sheets, some in fancy costumes, and others in European clothes which had been given to them. Kate never forgot the picturesque sight of Indians flocking to the mission on foot, in wagons, and on horseback.

With Father Stephan leading them, for Bishop O'Connor had gone back to Omaha, they rode on to Holy Rosary Mission, Pine Bluff Agency, and then to the Immaculate Conception Mission which Kate was building as a loving tribute to her mother.

Sometimes by horseback, sometimes by rail, and more than once by wagon, Kate and her sisters visited mission after mission. Everywhere they heard pleas for more sisters, more brothers, more priests.

It was late October when the Drexels returned to

St. Michel, but not to rest, for it was after this trip that the many Drexel Indian Schools, as they were called, came into existence.

Not long before General Custer's last stand at the Little Big Horn, President Grant had announced he would give a subsidy of $100 a pupil to any church group which would establish schools among the Indians. The interest of Kate and her sisters was now stimulated by the trip and by their firsthand observations of the need for schools, churches, and religious to staff them.

With the advice of Father Stephan, Kate bought property, erected buildings, and then deeded the structures and grounds to the Bureau of Catholic Indian Missions. Father Stephan then received a contract from the government entitling the bureau to the subsidy of $100 for each student in the schools. The only other task which faced Kate and the priest was to storm heaven and the heads of religious communities for priests and nuns.

In the summer of 1888, the Most Reverend P. J. Ryan, D.D., archbishop of Philadelphia, dedicated the St. Francis de Sales Industrial School at Eddington. The pupils of the new school, which was to be conducted by the Brothers of the Christian

Schools, were 200 boys selected from St. John's Orphan Asylum in Philadelphia.

Meanwhile, Louise, whose interest in the Josephites had continued, bought for the order a $59,000 property in Baltimore. This was the beginning of Epiphany College which was to train priests for work in the Negro apostolate.

When the Drexel girls were asked to support the projected Catholic University of America, they donated $50,000 for the establishment of the Francis A. Drexel chair of Moral Theology. Another $30,000 went to St. Agnes Hospital in Philadelphia in order that the Sisters of St. Francis might buy property for the expansion of the hospital.

Though Kate and her sisters found little time for society, youth is a time for romance, and the very year their benefactions reached a peak was also the year Louise Bouvier Drexel quietly announced her engagement to Edward Morrell. Soon after the bells rang to usher in the new year of 1889, wedding bells also rang.

The Nuptial Mass at the cathedral was celebrated by Bishop O'Connor, with Archbishop Ryan performing the marriage ceremony. Uncle Anthony gave the bride away. Kate, Elizabeth, and their cousins, Katherine Drexel and Lillie Dixon, were bridesmaids. Only relatives and a few intimate friends were invited to the breakfast at 1503.

When the bridal party reached the house, Kate managed to get a few moments with teary-eyed Johanna and Miss Cassidy, to whom Louise was still the baby. But Johanna cheered them up by recalling the night of Elizabeth's debut when each time Louise had attempted to snatch one of the delicacies from the serving table a swallow-tailed waiter had stopped her with a cold stare.

A hearty laugh broke the tension, and Kate rejoined the party before Louise and her young groom, Ned, stole away for their honeymoon.

Bishop O'Connor had arranged for Kate to enter the novitiate of the Sisters of Mercy in Pittsburgh before beginning her own special work. After Louise's marriage, Kate dreaded leaving Elizabeth alone, but she was eager to get started. Though the work with the Indians was going well, she was always aware of the need for more teachers. This was to be her special mission.

It was spring before the honeymooners started homeward. Mr. and Mrs. Morrell returned to Philadelphia, pausing only long enough to make plans

for setting up their own homes at South Rittenhouse Square and on a property adjoining St. Michel
which Louise had christened San José. Elizabeth,
Louise, and Ned were to make the trip to Pittsburgh
with Kate, and from there the three of them were
to go on to Europe.

In the meantime, the three sisters were together
again—with the addition of a new brother. Only the
realization that Kate was leaving them to seek her
own sanctification and to bring greater honor and
glory to God, by carrying the knowledge and love
of Him to the Indian and Negro people, softened
the sorrow of what was to be a final parting of the
ways.

On May 7, 1889, they left Philadelphia. At Pittsburgh, Elizabeth, Louise and Ned gave Kate into
the keeping of Mother Sebastian, the superior, and
Mother Inez, the Mistress of Novices. Kate radiated
the joy of one who has at long last had her heart's
desire fulfilled. The sisters and her new brother
were consoled by her happiness. They were glad,
though, that they would not have to return without
her to 1503 Chestnut Street, and grateful for the
foresight which had caused them to plan the European trip.

The young postulant, now Sister Mary Katharine, wrote often to the travelers with the permission of Mother Inez. She knew they were worried about her health, so she reassured them by writing cheerfully, giving vivid pictures of her daily life. When she was not sure of their address, she sent her letters to the faithful Johanna, who redirected them.

Sister Katharine's reception into the order was scheduled for November 7, 1889. Her family returned to the States in September, and Louise and Ned were delighted to find San José nearing completion.

Elizabeth made all of the preparations for the trip to Pittsburgh. With the aid of Uncle Anthony, a private car was chartered on the Pennsylvania Railroad. Besides Elizabeth, Louise, and Ned, many of the Drexel and Bouvier aunts, uncles and cousins, and a few intimate friends were aboard when the train left Philadelphia.

Elizabeth and Louise, happy that Kate's reception was to be a festive occasion, were sad, too, because some of the party made it clear they thought Kate had been heartless to leave Elizabeth. They were unaware that the older sister had a secret of her own which she had decided not to reveal until after the reception.

Bishop O'Connor and Father Stephan were

among those present in the chapel of the Convent of Mercy on November 7, 1889, when Kate Drexel became the bride of Christ.

Newspaper reporters had sought interviews with the Drexel heiress from the day she had arrived in Pittsburgh, but Mother Inez and Mother Sebastian had protected her from all publicity. They were even more careful at the time of the reception, and most of the wire services simply carried routine accounts of the ceremony, although some newspapers referred to Sister Katharine as "the world's richest nun."

On the return trip to Philadelphia, Elizabeth Drexel revealed her secret. She was engaged to Walter George Smith, a brilliant young attorney, and on January 7, 1890, there was a quiet country wedding in the little Church of St. Dominic near St. Michel. Though Sister Katharine could not be present, she was grateful to God that her beloved sister would not be alone or lonely. The last pebble has been removed from her pool of spiritual joy. Nothing could, or would, distract her from the work to which God, His Blessed Mother, St. Francis, the Holy Father, and Bishop O'Connor had directed her.

Chapter Eleven

Reunion

THE days moved swiftly for Sister Katharine. It would not be long before Lady Poverty, for whom St. Francis had held such great love, would be her daily companion. Surely, the young novice thought, her joy was boundless.

Meanwhile, Elizabeth and Louise were surveying literally the whole of Bucks County, Pennsylvania in search of a site for the home of the community which Sister Katharine was to establish. Shortly before Elizabeth left for a European honeymoon, she found a parcel of land at Andalusia—later to be Cornwells Heights—which Louise agreed would be ideal for a motherhouse. With the approval of Sister Katharine, the property was purchased. Plans moved forward, and the ground was broken while Elizabeth was still on her bridal trip.

The building program was a sweet excuse for the sisters to write each other often. There came a time, however, when no letters from the bride were delivered to the convent in Pittsburgh. Sister Katharine tried not to worry, but she knew this was unlike the thoughtful Elizabeth. Then came a message from Louise. Elizabeth was dangerously ill, and there was an ocean and a convent wall between them.

While Sister Katharine was storming heaven for her sister, Louise left for Europe. There were many days of anguished prayer until Sister Katharine heard that Elizabeth was out of danger.

The cup of sorrow was still not empty. In May, 1890, Sister Katharine's wisest of friends, Bishop O'Connor, answered the call of his Master. Though the young religious was saddened, it was soon apparent that she had won a powerful friend in heaven.

Not long after Bishop O'Connor's death, she received the apostolic blessing from her most Holy Father, Leo XIII, whose inspired counsel she had heeded.

Soon after the loss of Sister Katharine's spiritual adviser, her superior had the sad duty of telling her that Elizabeth Drexel Smith, only recently returned to St. Michel to await the birth of a child, had joined Francis and Emma Drexel in death.

Louise was still on her way home from Europe, and when Sister Katharine reached St. Michel, she had to push aside her own grief to comfort the heartbroken husband, who had lost wife and child, and to console Miss Cassidy and Johanna, who had been with Elizabeth until the end.

When Sister Katharine returned to Pittsburgh for the last months of her novitiate, a small part of her sorrow stemmed from the knowledge that Elizabeth's death had left dear old St. Michel empty. It was just as well that so many demands were made upon her time during the days that followed. Almost before she realized it, she was facing another of the important days of her life—the day on which she would pronounce her vows.

On February 12, 1891, in St. Mary's Chapel of

the Sisters of Mercy at Pittsburgh, Sister Mary Katharine took the vows of poverty, obedience, and chastity. She consecrated her life, and the fortune bequeathed her by her father, to the service of Indians and Negroes. Archbishop Ryan of Philadelphia, who had taken Bishop O'Connor's place as spiritual father to Sister Katharine, officiated at the ceremony. The archbishop immediately recognized Sister Katharine as foundress of the new community which was to be known as the Sisters of the Blessed Sacrament for Indians and Colored People. As the first superior general of the congregation, she became Reverend Mother M. Katharine Drexel.

Thirteen young women had answered Mother Katharine's call to prepare for this new work with Indians and Negroes. More and more the presence of the new superior was required to supervise the construction work at the motherhouse. Since Cornwells Heights was so near St. Michel, Mother Katharine decided to take her little band to Torresdale and use the Drexel home as a temporary novitiate until the new convent was completed. It was to be named St. Elizabeth's in honor of the sister who had first shared in the plans for the building.

By the fall of 1892, the motherhouse was ready, and there, in the archdiocese of Philadelphia, one of the greatest missionary efforts in the history of America began. As Mother Katharine's band continued to grow, she continued to travel from one end of America to the other, setting up missions and schools.

Mother Katharine was especially concerned about the Navaho Indians, a tribe poor both spiritually and materially. Thousands of them roamed the Arizona desert on a twelve-million-acre reservation, the greater part of it barren waste. The foundress of the Blessed Sacrament Sisters determined to build a school.

By the fall of 1902, the buildings which were to become St. Michael's Boarding School were nearing completion, and Mother Katharine started for Arizona to prepare living quarters for those who were to follow. After a stop at Santa Fe, where she and her companion visited a school Mother Katharine had already founded for the Pueblo Indians, they went on to Gallup, New Mexico. This was as far as the train would take them. On they went into Arizona, after having been met by a Franciscan father whose rectory was near the new school. The Franciscans had been sent to work among the Navahos as a result of Mother Katharine's pleas for priests.

For the thirty-mile drive out to St. Michael's, the priest had brought a light, horse-drawn spring wagon with two plank seats and no cover. If Mother Katharine compared the rattling wagon with the luxurious private car in which the Drexels had made their first trip to the far West, she gave no sign of it. Discomforts were soon forgotten as Mother Katharine and her companion, Mother Ignatius, admired the stark beauty of the hills and valleys and rode on into the heart of the wild desert.

It seemed to Mother Katharine that the horses were treading an ocean of sand. The red sandstone cliffs dwarfed the animals as well as the wagon and its occupants. As the sun sank behind the cliffs, Mother Katharine fingered the beads attached to the white cincture which girded the waist of her black habit.

It is so easy, she thought, to say the Rosary when one seems so alone with God.

Though the sun had disappeared when the party reached the priests' home, a bright moon silvered the sandy hill on which the house was perched. The sisters needed no lantern to find the path to the buildings which were to be St. Michael's.

Rooms for the sisters had been prepared in one of the cabins which had housed the workers. Enough moonlight shone into the dark log hut to allow Mother Katharine to find a lamp—but there was no oil in it. After discovering oil and matches, the sisters lit the lamp and looked around. The lamp rested on a square kitchen table in the middle of the room. One armchair was the only other furnishing. The floor would never have to be scrubbed or waxed. It was dirt—hard, even, and compact. The tiny adjoining room was bare except for two cots.

The next day Mother Katharine learned that the region had suffered a drought and that the corn she had instructed a farmer to plant had not come up. She had depended on the shucks from this corn to serve as stuffing for the hundred or more mattresses they would need for the Indian children.

Mother Katharine was told, too, that the men had been unable to find water except for the shallow well which barely supplied the priests. She immediately wrote the motherhouse and asked the sisters to pray for water and mattress stuffing. Then she dispatched one of the workmen to Gallup with instructions to go on to Santa Fe, if necessary, to find the proper machinery to drill for water.

As a substitute for the shucks from the corn that never grew, Mother Katharine decided to try sheared wool. After a half pound was secured for the test, it had to be washed. Back and forth from the priests' well the sisters carried bucket after bucket of water. Four times they rubbed and soaped the wool with amole plant, but the sheepy smell defied water and soap. They had been so engrossed in their experiment that neither sister noticed they had been spilling water. By the time they did notice, the floor had become a muddy puddle. After half a day, all the sisters had to show for their work was the un-pleasant-smelling wool and two pairs of muddy black shoes.

The water situation remained serious. When it seemed almost hopeless, Mother Katharine asked one of the priests to drive her to the nearest church at Newton. As she begged God for water, she thought about our Lord at the well in Samaria, sitting there, tired and weary, asking the woman to give Him to drink. She remembered that He had said, "If thou didst know the gift of God . . . thou wouldst rather have asked of Him living waters."

"O Lord," Mother Katharine prayed, "forgive me for asking for temporal waters rather than waters of abundant grace for the missionaries and the waters of baptism for the Navahos."

A few evenings later, Mother Katharine sat in the little dirt-floored cabin studying plans for the badly needed water system. Suddenly she heard the sound of trickling water. A stream was advancing across the floor toward her. The drought was over; the rain had come. On the feast of St. Michael, September 29, Mother Katharine directed the men as they drilled successfully for water.

The hundreds of Navaho boys and girls who have attended St. Michael's, now a modern elementary and high school, enjoy an abundance of temporal, as well as spiritual, waters. This is the legacy they received from Mother Katharine and the Sisters of the Blessed Sacrament.

Great distances had to be spanned to reach the Indians, but needy Negroes were ever at Mother Katharine's door. Even during the days of the temporary novitiate at St. Michel, a group of colored orphans had been housed in the gardener's cottage. These children were the first to occupy Holy Providence House which became a boarding school for Negro boys and girls.

At the turn of the century, Mother Katharine realized the need to prepare Negro girls to go out and work among their own people. She purchased a tract of land at Rock Castle, forty miles from Richmond, Virginia, near the home of the Indian maiden, Pocahontas. This site, on the southern bank of the historic James River, became the home of St. Francis de Sales Institute, now St. Francis de Sales High School. The massive red brick building soon was known as The Castle. Here thousands of Negro girls have been trained.

Mrs. Morrell and her husband, continuing to share every interest of their saintly sister, purchased a vast estate, Belmead, about a mile away from St. Francis de Sales. This sprawling old plantation became the home of St. Emma Industrial and Agricultural Institute where Negro boys are instructed in crafts and trades.

In 1915, the archbishop of New Orleans, the Most Reverend James S. Blenk, asked Mother Katharine to undertake the education of Negro youth in New Orleans. Southern University had moved to Baton Rouge, and Reverend Mother Katharine purchased that property for the new Xavier Secondary School. This preparatory school was the forerunner of Xavier University.

Now located at Palmetto Street near Carrollton Avenue, Xavier occupies approximately eight city blocks. The university comprises a college of liberal arts and sciences, a college of pharmacy, a school of education, a graduate school, and seven special departments.

As Negroes crowded urban centers during the northern migrations which followed World War I, Mother Katharine sent her teaching daughters into these cities to staff parochial schools.

The work with Negroes did not prevent the Sisters of the Blessed Sacrament from continuing their missionary efforts among the Indians. A spokesman for the Bureau of Catholic Indian Missions once said that every Catholic mission for Indians had, at one time or another, been aided by Mother Katharine Drexel.

Though walking daily with Lady Poverty, Mother Katharine held her millions in trust for the Indian and Negro. In 1921 Congress passed a law—and some say it was with Mother Katharine's fortune in mind—which freed charitable contributions from taxation.

Whenever a polite reference was made to the vast wealth Mother Katharine had renounced, she was quick to remind her listeners that she had given up only what every other Sister of the Blessed Sacrament gave up—everything she had. As missions were opened in Nashville, New Orleans, New York, Philadelphia, Boston, Cleveland, Cincinnati, and

Port Arthur, Mother Katharine continued to shun publicity and public attention. "It is better to do things quietly," was advice her associates were to hear over and over.

Mother Katharine denied herself many of the material comforts which she provided for each of her daughters. It is said that the foundress of the Sisters of the Blessed Sacrament was always the nun who looked least the way Reverend Mother Katharine Drexel would be expected to look. She wore the habit alloted to her until it was threadbare. On visitations to the far-flung Indian missions she preferred a day coach to the comforts of a Pullman. She usually carried her lunch neatly wrapped in brown paper.

The Rule of the new congregation received the Decree of Final Approbation on May 15, 1913, during the reign of Pope St. Pius X. From Popes Benedict XV, Pius XI, and Pius XII Mother Katharine received letters of commendation for her work and for that of her congregation.

The Sisters of the Blessed Sacrament celebrated the golden jubilee of their founding in 1941. Among the many who attended the ceremonies at the motherhouse were hundreds of Negroes and Indians who might never have come to know and love God without the help of Mother Katharine and her daughters.

When Louise Drexel Morrell died in 1945, Mother Katharine became the sole recipient of income from an accumulated $15,000,000 trust fund left by their father. By the terms of his will, the fortune was to be divided among twenty-nine charities after the death of his daughters, provided they left no heirs.

The labors and sacrifices of years began to weaken Mother Katharine, and, in 1937, she retired as superior general of the order. But she was a victim of old age only in body; her spirit remained young. Those who were privileged to visit her were imbued with the fragrance of her love for our divine Lord. It almost seemed as if she elected to spend her last days on an invalid's bed in order that her zealous daughters might mend any loose fences and be soundly established financially before she went home to heaven and they were deprived of her income. That income is estimated to have been $1,000 a day.

Priests who visited Mother Katharine during her last years say that they often saw her kissing the picture of the Sacred Heart and that she smiled as she showed them a little card bearing the likeness of

Pope Pius X. Sometimes it was as if Mother Katharine were whispering to her sainted friend, telling
him not to be impatient, for her work was not yet
finished.

Late in February, 1955, a common cold weakened Mother Katharine, but there seemed to be no
cause for alarm. Father Louis Pastorelli had visited
Reverend Mother each year, his visit always coming around the middle of March. While their superior was recovering from this cold, the sisters
were surprised to see Father Pastorelli, who presented himself two weeks before he was expected.
The morning after his arrival, as the priest stood beside the little bed which had become an altar of
sacrifice for Mother Katharine, it was obvious that
she shared the other sisters' surprise.

"You've come early," she said to the priest.

"Yes," he answered, "something seemed to im-
pel me to come earlier this year."

Mother Katharine smiled, but the smile was for
her departed loved ones who were waiting. She
wanted to be with them all. With them she wanted
to see our Lord and His Blessed Mother. Her wish
was a prayer which God saw fit to hear. On March
3, 1955, Reverend Mother Mary Katharine Drexel,
in the ninety-seventh year of her life, passed into

eternity as her loyal daughters and a beloved priest said the prayers of Holy Mother the Church.

A solemn Pontifical Requiem Mass for Mother Katharine was offered by Archbishop John F. O'Hara in the Cathedral of Saints Peter and Paul, Philadelphia. The cathedral was filled to overflowing with bishops, clergy, religious, and dignitaries from all professions and trades. Negroes and Indians from all over the United States journeyed to Philadelphia to pay last respects to their benefactress. In death Mother Katharine was returned to the motherhouse at Cornwells Heights and her remains interred in a crypt beneath the chapel.

Mother Katharine, who had started out with a little band of thirteen, left almost six hundred Sisters of the Blessed Sacrament to carry on her work. In addition to the motherhouse, there are forty-nine convents and sixty-one schools for Indians and Negroes. The "richest nun in the world" had given the treasure of treasures—the knowledge of God—to America's children of color.

Mother Katharine had lived to see her work receive popular acclaim. The Alliance of Catholic Women presented her with an award for being "Philadelphia's Great Lady." The President of Haiti journeyed to the motherhouse to bestow per-

sonally upon Mother Katharine the Honor of Merit
Medal from his republic. But perhaps the most fit-
ting tribute to the patriotic, "flag-waving" Kate
Drexel is one of which she herself and the members
of her community were unaware. She is pictured
with a group of notable American sons and daughters of the Church under the arch which forms the
main entrance to St. Matthew's Cathedral in Washington, D.C.

Mother Katharine's daughters and the children
who inherited from her the precious gift of faith
have reason to believe that they have gained a solic-
itous friend in heaven. In the words of Father
Pastorelli, they look forward to the day when they
can say, "I, personally, knew Saint Katharine
Drexel."

VISION BOOKS